Developing Skills in
ALGEBRA ONE

Harold Taylor ■ Loretta Taylor

Book A

DALE SEYMOUR PUBLICATIONS

Cover Design: Michael Rogondino
Technical Illustrations: Pat Rogondino
Typesetting: Beverly Page

ISBN 0-86651-221-7
Printed in the United States of America
    21 22 23 24 25   07 06 05 04

1-800-321-3106
www.pearsonlearning.com

CONTENTS

Introduction   v

Introduction to Algebra

Simplifying Numerical Expressions   1
Evaluating Variable Expressions   5
Using Formulas   7
Exponents   9
Evaluating Formulas   11
Grouping Symbols   13
Inserting Parentheses   15
Grouping Symbols   17

The Integers

Directed Distance   19
Graphing Integers   21
Absolute Value *(expressions and equations)*   23
Absolute Value *(graphs)*   25
Addition of Integers *(in pairs)*   27
Addition of Integers *(in fours)*   29
Addition of Integers *(completing equations)*   33
Subtraction of Integers   35
Addition and Subtraction of Integers *(in pairs)*   37
Addition and Subtraction of Integers *(pairs and triples)*   39
Addition and Subtraction of Integers *(multiple terms)*   41
Multiplication of Integers   43
Evaluating Variable Expressions   45

The Rationals

Reciprocals   47
Operations with Numbers   49
Number Properties   51
Using Number Properties   53

(over)

Algebraic Expressions and Equations

Combining Like Terms   55
Checking for Solutions   57
Solutions of Equations *(add or subtract)*   59
Solutions of Equations *(multiply or divide)*   63
Solutions of Equations *(add/subtract and multiply/divide)*   67
Solutions of Equations *(with like terms)*   71
Solutions of Equations *(with grouped terms)*   73
Solutions of Equations *(with variable on both sides)*   75
Writing and Solving Equations   77
Solving Equations Having More Than One Variable   79
Translating Word Expressions   83
Translating Algebraic Expressions   87
Translating Sentences into Equations   89

Word Problems

Number Problems   91
Problem Solving with Equations *(single-term equations)*   93
Motion Problems   95
Consecutive Integer Problems   99
Problem Solving with Equations *(multiple-term equations)*   101
Coin Problems   103
Angle Problems   105

Answers   107

INTRODUCTION

In order to master algebra, most students need a great deal of practice—practice allowing them to discover mathematical patterns, to make generalizations, and to consolidate their mathematical learning—practice that helps them see and understand the workings of algebra. Algebra textbooks, by their very nature, cannot provide the quantity of problems necessary for a beginning algebra course. In order to cover the complete range of problems related to a topic, most textbook exercise sets move very quickly from simple to complex problems, giving only a few of those in-between bread-and-butter problems that students need. As a result, algebra teachers are continually looking for problems to supplement their texts.

About the Series

Developing Skills in Algebra One was created primarily to help teachers in their search for extra algebra problems. The series was not designed to be a classroom text, rather it is a back-up resource containing problems for class examples, chalkboard work, quizzes, test preparation, and extra practice. *Developing Skills in Algebra One* is a four-book series of reproducible worksheets that provides extensive practice in all the work covered in the traditional first high school course in algebra.

Book A starts at the beginning of the school year with exercises in simplifying numerical expressions, and continues through to simple equations in one variable.

Book B includes operations with polynomials, factoring polynomials, solving polynomial equations, and working with rational expressions.

Book C covers ratio, proportion, graphing linear equations, solving systems of linear equations, plus inequalities and absolute value equations.

Book D completes the algebra one course with roots and radicals, quadratic equations, and analysis of quadratic functions.

By design, the books in the *Developing Skills in Algebra One* series are appropriate for use in any algebra one course, whether it is taught in ninth grade, tenth grade, seventh or eighth grade, or in a two-year algebra program. The books also provide review work for second-year algebra students, practice for students studying high school algebra at the college level, and exercises for adults reviewing algebra on their own.

Pick-and-Choose Pages

Book A is the first book in the *Developing Skills in Algebra One* series. It contains 106 worksheets with more than 2500 problems that you can duplicate and use with your students. There is no required order for presenting the exercises in this book but, for maximum convenience, the worksheets are arranged sequentially, concept by concept. You may choose to select worksheets from the book as back-up for your algebra lessons. You might assign a worksheet to a single student who needs practice in a specific skill. Or, you may decide to keep certain pages as your own personal resource of problems on a particular topic. The contents in the front of this book and the labels at the top of each worksheet page will help you identify the exercises that best meet your needs.

Paired Worksheets and Exercises

As you glance through this book, you will discover that the worksheets come in pairs; there are at least two parallel worksheets for every concept so that students can learn on one set of problems and practice on the next. Several pairs of worksheets are included for particularly troublesome topics. Each pair of worksheets practices only one or two specific skills (noted at the top left of the pages), carefully sequenced and organized. Most worksheet exercises are also paired, by odds and evens, to allow for two-day assignments or for practice and testing. And, clear simple worksheet instructions along with handwritten samples of the exercises allow students to get right to work with a minimum of fuss.

Checking Work

In order to provide a quantity of problems—enough problems on a page to make it worth copying—and in order to give you complete coverage of algebra topics, we have limited the amount of workspace allowed for some exercises. We suggest that you have students show all their work on separate sheets of paper, but transfer their answers to the worksheets. You (or your students) will have a quick way to check answers as well as access to the work you must see to diagnose students' errors of understanding.

You will find answers to every problem in this book. The answers are located after the worksheet pages.

About Practice

Practice is an important part of learning, but it's not the only part. Practice makes sense only after instruction and demonstrated understanding. To help students master algebra, we must aim for a regular and consistent blend of practice with meaningful instruction, taking pains to individualize practice as much as possible. *Developing Skills in Algebra One* is one tool you can use to achieve that goal, but it is just a tool. The hard work and dedication are up to you and your students.

Developing Skills in

ALGEBRA ONE

Simplifying Numerical Expressions   Name _____

Date _____ Period _____

Simplify.

1. $0.5 + 0.5$ _1.0_   **2.** $0.8 + 0.8$ _____

3. $1571 - 1570$ _____   **4.** $1736 - 1544$ _____

5. $1000 \div 1000$ _____   **6.** $544 \div 544$ _____

7. $1 \cdot 1 \cdot 1 \cdot 1$ _____   **8.** $0 \cdot 0 \cdot 0 \cdot 0$ _____

9. $3 - 2$ _____   **10.** $9 - 5$ _____

11. $1 + 0 + 0$ _____   **12.** $0 + 1 + 1$ _____

13. $4 + 4 + 4 + 4$ _____   **14.** $6 + 6 + 6 + 6$ _____

15. $12 + 46$ _____   **16.** $29 + 43$ _____

Tell whether each statement is true or false.

17. $3 = 5 + 2$ T (F)   **18.** $25(6) = 6(25)$ T   F

19. $5 + 6 = 12 - 1$ T   F   **20.** $14 + 13 = 7 + 13 + 7$ T   F

21. $15 + 16 = 16 + 15$ T   F   **22.** $18 + 18 = 36(2)$ T   F

23. $12(12) = 3(48)$ T   F   **24.** $200 - 100 = 100 - 200$ T   F

25. $12 \div 3 = 36 \div 6$ T   F   **26.** $2(5)(5) = 5(5)(2)$ T   F

27. $25 + 25 = 2(25)$ T   F   **28.** $25 \div 5 = 75 \div 3$ T   F

29. $19 - 12 = 12 - 19$ T   F   **30.** $82 \div 2 = 84 \div 4$ T   F

31. $5(6) = 6(5)$ T   F   **32.** $25 + 32 = 2(28)$ T   F

Simplifying Numerical Expressions

Name _____

Date _____ Period _____

Simplify.

1. $2 \cdot 2 \cdot 2 \cdot 2$ *16*

2. $5 \cdot 5 \cdot 5 \cdot 5$ _____

3. $13 \cdot 17$ _____

4. $25 \cdot 32$ _____

5. $169 \div 13$ _____

6. $225 \div 15$ _____

7. $3 + 4 + 5 + 6$ _____

8. $2 + 4 + 6 + 8$ _____

9. $10(20)(30)$ _____

10. $2(4)(8)(16)$ _____

11. $12 + 14 - 7 - 6$ _____

12. $8 + 10 - 5 - 4$ _____

13. $3 \cdot 3 \cdot 3 \cdot 3 \cdot 3$ _____

14. $2 \cdot 2 \cdot 2 \cdot 2 \cdot 2$ _____

15. $1011 - 997$ _____

16. $1436 - 285$ _____

Tell whether each statement is true or false.

17. $8 = 5 + 3$ (T) F

18. $23(2) = 3(22)$ T F

19. $8 + 15 = 30 - 7$ T F

20. $15 + 12 = 6 + 15 + 6$ T F

21. $2 + 4 + 6 + 8 = 20$ T F

22. $5 + 10 + 15 + 20 = 60$ T F

23. $2(3)(4)(5) = 240$ T F

24. $5(2)(3)(6) = 180$ T F

25. $13 - 7 = 7 - 13$ T F

26. $45 - 10 = 10 - 45$ T F

27. $26 + 43 = 43 + 26$ T F

28. $15 + 29 = 29 + 15$ T F

29. $12 \div 6 = 6 \div 12$ T F

30. $35 \div 7 = 7 \div 35$ T F

31. $13(25) = 25(13)$ T F

32. $43(16) = 16(43)$ T F

Simplifying Numerical Expressions

Name _____

Date _____ Period _____

Tell how many terms are in each expression, then evaluate the expression.

1. $6(3) + 8(2)$ _2_ _34_

2. $4(2)(5) - 13(2)$ _____ _____

3. $15 + 4(3) + 8$ _____ _____

4. $2(2)(2)(2) + 3(3)$ _____ _____

5. $25 \div 5 + 28 \div 4$ _____ _____

6. $65 - 14(3) + 8$ _____ _____

7. $6 + 8(2) - 15 \div 3$ _____ _____

8. $21 \div 3 + 8(2) - 15$ _____ _____

Simplify each term and then combine terms.

9. $5(2) + 3(7) + 4$ _35_

10. $35 + 4(3) - 24 \div 8$ _____

11. $7 + 9(3) + 15 \div 3$ _____

12. $17 + 8(2) + 13$ _____

13. $35 + 7(3) - 21 \div 7$ _____

14. $49 - 16(2) + 10$ _____

15. $3(7)(5) - 16(3)$ _____

16. $12 + 13(5) + 27 \div 9$ _____

17. $38 \div 2 + 56 \div 7$ _____

18. $56 \div 4 + 17(2) - 37$ _____

19. $3(3)(3) + 5(5)$ _____

20. $35 \div 7 + 18 \div 9$ _____

Tell how many factors are in each expression and evaluate.

21. $2(3)(7)$ _3_ _42_

22. $17(6)(2)(4)$ _____ _____

23. $5(5)(9)13$ _____ _____

24. $6(7)(15)$ _____ _____

25. $11(17)$ _____ _____

26. $12(92)(6)$ _____ _____

27. $3(17)(29)(31)$ _____ _____

28. $59(2)$ _____ _____

29. $43(5)$ _____ _____

30. $12(6)(9)$ _____ _____

Simplifying Numerical Expressions

Name _____

Date _____ Period _____

Tell how many terms are in each expression, then evaluate the expression.

1. $8(2) + 9(5)$ _2_ _61_   **2.** $6(3)(2) - 12(3)$ _____ _____

3. $17 + 5(7) + 2$ _____ _____   **4.** $3(3)(3)(3) + 4(4)$ _____ _____

5. $35 \div 5 + 28 \div 4$ _____ _____   **6.** $54 - 11(3) + 5$ _____ _____

7. $9 + 7(3) - 18 \div 6$ _____ _____   **8.** $36 \div 6 + 9(2) - 13$ _____ _____

Simplify each term and then combine terms.

9. $7(4) + 2(8) + 9$ _53_   **10.** $26 + 3(7) - 33 \div 3$ _____

11. $9 + 7(6) + 24 \div 3$ _____   **12.** $21 + 5(7) + 8$ _____

13. $46 + 5(4) - 40 \div 5$ _____   **14.** $63 - 18(2) + 12$ _____

15. $2(9)(4) - 18(3)$ _____   **16.** $14 + 15(3) + 30 \div 6$ _____

17. $42 \div 2 + 81 \div 9$ _____   **18.** $56 \div 8 + 14(3) - 28$ _____

19. $2(2)(2) + 7(7)$ _____   **20.** $39 \div 3 + 35 \div 7$ _____

Tell how many factors are in each expression and evaluate.

21. $5(2)(9)(3)$ _4_ _270_   **22.** $13(5)(6)$ _____ _____

23. $5(5)(9)$ _____ _____   **24.** $6(7)(12)(2)$ _____ _____

25. $21(15)$ _____ _____   **26.** $15(31)(8)(6)$ _____ _____

27. $4(18)(14)$ _____ _____   **28.** $51(5)(16)$ _____ _____

29. $23(8)(11)$ _____ _____   **30.** $32(5)(2)$ _____ _____

Evaluating Variable Expressions

Evaluate if $a = 3$ and $b = 5$.

1. $12 + a$ _15_   **2.** $a + b$ _____

3. $65 + b$ _____   **4.** $b - a$ _____

5. $46 - b$ _____   **6.** ab _____

7. $125 - a$ _____   **8.** $7ab$ _____

9. $15a$ _____   **10.** $45 \div ab$ _____

11. $130 \div b$ _____   **12.** $15a \div b$ _____

Evaluate if $x = 7$, $y = 9$, $z = 3$ and $u = 1$.

13. $z - z$ _O_   **14.** $y - x$ _____

15. $72uz$ _____   **16.** uzx _____

17. $x + y + z - u$ _____   **18.** $u + y + x - z$ _____

19. $2x + 2x + 2x$ _____   **20.** $2x + 2y + u$ _____

21. $u + 2y + z - 2z$ _____   **22.** $4x - 2y - 2z - 2u$ _____

23. $(y - x)(z - u)$ _____   **24.** $(x - z)(y - u)$ _____

25. $(y + u) \div (z + x)$ _____   **26.** $(y + z) \div (x - u)$ _____

27. $xy \div z$ _____   **28.** $yu \div z$ _____

29. $xy - 6z$ _____   **30.** $4x - yz$ _____

Evaluating Variable Expressions

Evaluate if $a = 3$ and $b = 5$.

1. $15 + b$ _20_

2. $2a - b$ _____

3. $37 + a$ _____

4. $7b - a$ _____

5. $23 - a$ _____

6. $4ab$ _____

7. $112 - b$ _____

8. $127 - a$ _____

9. $35a$ _____

10. $105 \div ab$ _____

11. $132 \div a$ _____

12. $45b \div a$ _____

Evaluate if $x = 7$, $y = 9$, $z = 3$ and $u = 1$.

13. $y - z$ _6_

14. $x - u$ _____

15. $138 \div z$ _____

16. $945 \div y$ _____

17. $z + x - y + u$ _____

18. $x + x + x + x$ _____

19. $z - u + x + z$ _____

20. $y - u - x + z$ _____

21. $2y - 2x - u$ _____

22. $2x + 2y - 2z$ _____

23. $xy - 16$ _____

24. $yz - 20$ _____

25. $(x + y) \div 2$ _____

26. $(y + u) \div 5$ _____

27. $(y - z) \div (z - u)$ _____

28. $(x + z) \div (y + u)$ _____

29. $5x - 3y + \dfrac{6z}{y}$ _____

30. $7y - 4x + \dfrac{7u}{x}$ _____

Using Formulas   Name _____

Date _____ Period _____

AREA AND PERIMETER OF A RECTANGLE

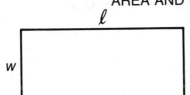

ℓ = length w = width

A = area P = perimeter

$A = \ell w$ $P = 2(\ell + w)$

Find the areas and perimeters of the rectangles given in the tables below.

	ℓ	w	A	P
1.	5	15	75	40
3.	10	100		
5.	150	250		

	ℓ	w	A	P
2.	7	62		
4.	100	200		
6.	75	145		

AREA AND PERIMETER OF A SQUARE

s = side

A = area P = perimeter

$A = s \times s$ $P = 4s$

Find the areas and perimeters for squares given in the tables below.

	s	A	P
7.	5		
9.	10		
11.	77		

	s	A	P
8.	7		
10.	26		
12.	52		

AREA AND PERIMETER OF A RIGHT TRIANGLE

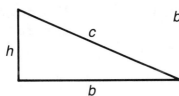

b = base h = height c = hypotenuse

A = area P = perimeter

$A = \frac{1}{2}bh$ $P = b + h + c$

Find the areas and perimeters for right triangles given in the tables below.

	b	h	c	A	P
13.	3	4	5		
15.	8	15	17		
17.	10	24	26		

	b	h	c	A	P
14.	5	12	13		
16.	11	29	31		
18.	7	24	25		

     7

Name _____

Date _____ Period _____

AREA AND PERIMETER OF AN ISOSCELES TRAPEZOID

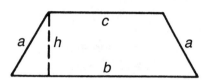

A = area P = perimeter

$A = \dfrac{h}{2}(b + c)$ $P = 2a + b + c$

Find the areas and perimeters of the trapezoids given in the tables below.

	a	b	c	h	A	P
1.	5	10	4	4	28	24
3.	15	28	10	12		
5.	25	46	16	20		

	a	b	c	h	A	P
2.	10	20	8	8		
4.	20	36	12	16		
6.	17	23	19	12		

AREA AND PERIMETER OF A PARALLELOGRAM

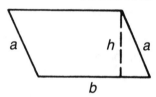

A = area P = perimeter

$A = bh$ $P = 2(a + b)$

Find the areas and perimeters for parallelograms given in the tables below.

	a	b	h	A	P
7.	2	5	1		
9.	5	8	4		
11.	6	12	4		

	a	b	h	A	P
8.	4	7	3		
10.	7	10	5		
12.	15	18	11		

AREA AND CIRCUMFERENCE OF A CIRCLE

r = radius A = area C = circumference

π = pi $A = \pi \cdot r \cdot r$ $C = 2\pi r$

Find the areas and circumferences for circles given in the tables below.

	r	A	C
13.	7		
15.	14		
17.	3.5		

	r	A	C
14.	21		
16.	28		
18.	5.6		

Exponents

Name _____

Date _____ Period _____

Rewrite using exponents.

1. aaaaaaa a^7

2. ccccc   _____

3. aabbbb   _____

4. aaaabbb   _____

5. aabbccc   _____

6. aaabcccc   _____

7. 3xxyyyz   _____

8. 7xyyyyzz   _____

Rewrite without using exponents.

9. $4x^2y^2$ $4xxyy$

10. $10x^3y^2z$ _____

11. $3a^3b^2c$ _____

12. $5a^2b^3c^2$ _____

13. $2m^4n$ _____

14. $9r^3s^3t^2$ _____

15. $7bc^4$ _____

16. $13p^4q$ _____

17. $6ab(8a^2b)$ _____

18. $3x^3(5y)(2x^4)$ _____

19. $5x^3y^2(2x^2y^3)$ _____

20. $7a^4b^2(2a^2b)(3b)$ _____

21. $8m^2n^3(2m^2n)(3n)$ _____

22. $14r^3s^2t^2(2r^2s^3t)$ _____

Evaluate if $a = 2$, $b = 4$, and $c = 5$.

23. $7a^2b^2c$ 2240

24. $5a^3b^2c^2$ _____

25. $4a^4b^2c$ _____

26. $9a^3b^3c^2$ _____

27. $11a^4b$ _____

28. $3b^2c^3$ _____

29. $6a^5c$ _____

30. $4a^7c^2$ _____

Exponents

Name _____

Date _____ Period _____

Rewrite using exponents.

1. $mmmmm$ m^5

2. $rrrrrrr$ _____

3. $xxxyyy$ _____

4. $ccddddd$ _____

5. $mmmnn$ _____

6. $rrssst$ _____

7. $6mnnnn$ _____

8. $5aaaabbcc$ _____

Rewrite without using exponents.

9. $2m^2n^2$ $2mmnn$

10. $12a^3b^2c^2$ _____

11. $5x^3y^2z$ _____

12. $9r^2s^3t^2$ _____

13. $4a^2b^3c^4$ _____

14. $8p^2q^4$ _____

15. $9m^3n^2$ _____

16. $18c^2d^3$ _____

17. $4xy(3x^2y^2)$ _____

18. $7m^2(8n^2)(3m^3n^2)$ _____

19. $3a^2b^2(7a^3b^3)$ _____

20. $2c^2d^3(2c^2d)(3d)$ _____

21. $6r^2s^2(5r^2s)(2s)$ _____

22. $16a^3b^2c^2(5a^2b^2c^2)$ _____

Evaluate if $a = 3$, $b = 2$, and $c = 4$.

23. $2a^2b^3c$ 576

24. $7a^3b^2c^2$ _____

25. $5a^2b^4c$ _____

26. $8a^2b^3c^2$ _____

27. $14a^5b$ _____

28. $9b^6c$ _____

29. $3a^2b^2$ _____

30. $14a^3c^2$ _____

10

Evaluating Formulas

Name _____

Date _____ Period _____

VOLUME AND SURFACE AREA OF A CUBE

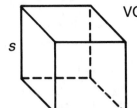

s = side V = volume S = surface area
                  $V = s^3$ $S = 6s^2$

Find the volumes and surface areas for the cubes given in the tables below.

	s	V	S
1.	3	27	54
3.	5		
5.	15		

	s	V	S
2.	7		
4.	9		
6.	11		

VOLUME AND SURFACE AREA OF A RECTANGULAR PRISM

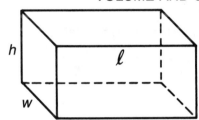

ℓ = length V = volume S = surface area
w = width $V = \ell \cdot w \cdot h$ $S = 2(\ell w + hw + \ell h)$
h = height

Find the volumes and surface areas for the rectangular prisms given in the tables below.

	ℓ	w	h	V	S
7.	2	3	5		
9.	7	2	11		
11.	11	6	13		

	ℓ	w	h	V	S
8.	4	10	9		
10.	8	5	13		
12.	21	6	22		

VOLUME AND SURFACE AREA OF A CYLINDER

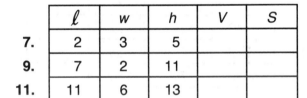

r = radius V = volume S = surface area
h = height $V = \pi r^2 h$ $S = 2\pi rh$

Find the volumes and surface areas for the cylinders given in the tables below. Use $\frac{22}{7}$ for π.

	r	h	V	S
13.	21	5		
15.	11	21		
17.	12	28		

	r	h	V	S
14.	9	14		
16.	8	35		
18.	4	42		

Name _____

Date _____ Period _____

LINEAR EQUATION PROBLEMS

Complete the tables below using the formula $y = mx + b$.

	m	x	b	y
1.	10	3	17	47
3.	0.9	15	5.6	
5.	$\frac{3}{4}$	24	32	

	m	x	b	y
2.	12	7	19	
4.	0.11	8	0.24	
6.	$\frac{2}{3}$	18	29	

INVESTMENT PROBLEMS (SIMPLE INTEREST)

p = principal (in dollars)
r = rate (expressed as a percent; change to decimal for doing arithmetic)
t = time (expressed in years)
i = simple interest (expressed in dollars)
formula: $i = prt$

Complete the tables below. Express the answers in dollars.

	p	r	t	i
7.	$560	14%	7 y	
9.	$398	18%	4 y	
11.	$876	13%	12 y	

	p	r	t	i
8.	$340	12%	9 y	
10.	$762	15%	5 y	
12.	$549	17%	14 y	

MOTION PROBLEMS

r = rate (expressed in distance per time unit)
t = time (expressed in minutes, hours, etc.)
d = distance (expressed in miles, kilometers, feet, etc.)
formulas: $d = rt$ $t = \frac{d}{r}$ $r = \frac{d}{t}$

Complete the following table. Write units with all answers.

	r	t	d
13.	35 mi/h	11 h	
15.		3 h	1128 mi
17.	93 km/h		1209 km

	r	t	d
14.	76 mi/h	15 h	
16.		7 h	5124 mi
18.	110 km/h		1870 km

Grouping Symbols

Name _____

Date _____ Period _____

Simplify.

1. $(4-2)$ _____2_____   **2.** $(7-3)$ _____

3. $16-(4-2)$ _____   **4.** $25-(7-3)$ _____

5. $(16-4)-2$ _____   **6.** $(25-7)-3$ _____

7. $6+(10-2)$ _____   **8.** $14+(9-3)$ _____

9. $(6+10)-2$ _____   **10.** $(14+9)-3$ _____

11. $5+(3\cdot5)$ _____   **12.** $9+(6\cdot8)$ _____

13. $(5+3)\cdot5$ _____   **14.** $(9+6)\cdot8$ _____

15. $[10-(4-2)]$ _____   **16.** $[25-(7-3)]$ _____

17. $16-[10-(4-2)]$ _____   **18.** $23-[25-(7-3)]$ _____

19. $75\div[(125\div5)-20]$ _____   **20.** $72\div[(136\div8)-8]$ _____

21. $(42\div7-24\div8)\div3$ _____   **22.** $(56\div4-30\div5)-2$ _____

23. $(4\cdot10-12\div3)\div6$ _____   **24.** $(6\cdot7-18\div6)\div3$ _____

25. $(56\div7+2)\div(30\div6)$ _____   **26.** $(84\div12+5)\div(28\div7)$ _____

27. $42-[169\div(7+6)]$ _____   **28.** $62-[225\div(8+7)]$ _____

29. $26-(17-8\div2)$ _____   **30.** $75-(72-8\cdot9)$ _____

31. $18\div[24\div(12\div3)]$ _____   **32.** $48\div[36\div(42\div7)]$ _____

33. $10\cdot3\div(8-2)$ _____   **34.** $4\cdot5\div(13-3)$ _____

Grouping Symbols

Name _____

Date _____ Period _____

Simplify.

1. $(8 - 1)$ _7_   **2.** $(9 - 4)$ _____

3. $18 - (8 - 1)$ _____   **4.** $33 - (9 - 4)$ _____

5. $(18 - 8) - 1$ _____   **6.** $(33 - 9) - 4$ _____

7. $9 + (15 - 3)$ _____   **8.** $22 + (25 - 8)$ _____

9. $(9 + 15) - 2$ _____   **10.** $(22 + 25) - 8$ _____

11. $6 + (4 \cdot 7)$ _____   **12.** $12 + (10 \cdot 8)$ _____

13. $(6 + 4) \cdot 7$ _____   **14.** $(12 + 10) \cdot 8$ _____

15. $[10 - (8 - 1)]$ _____   **16.** $[25 - (9 - 4)]$ _____

17. $16 - [10 - (8 - 1)]$ _____   **18.** $42 - [25 - (9 - 4)]$ _____

19. $84 \div [(100 \div 4) - 13]$ _____   **20.** $95 \div [(132 \div 6) - 3]$ _____

21. $(48 \div 8 - 27 \div 9) \div 3$ _____   **22.** $(62 \div 2 - 32 \div 8) - 9$ _____

23. $(3 \cdot 12 - 22 \div 2) \div 5$ _____   **24.** $(9 \cdot 5 - 24 \div 4) \div 3$ _____

25. $(48 \div 6 + 2) \div (25 \div 5)$ _____   **26.** $(56 \div 14 + 7) \div (55 \div 5)$ _____

27. $84 - [144 \div (8 + 4)]$ _____   **28.** $62 - [105 \div (9 + 6)]$ _____

29. $45 - (32 - 9 \div 3)$ _____   **30.** $93 - (41 - 6 \cdot 3)$ _____

31. $32 \div [16 \div (8 \div 2)]$ _____   **32.** $56 \div [48 \div (84 \div 7)]$ _____

33. $12 \cdot 5 \div (12 - 2)$ _____   **34.** $8 \cdot 6 \div (24 - 8)$ _____

Inserting Parentheses

Name _____

Date _____ Period _____

Simplify.

1. $(2 \cdot 3) + 5$ _//_

2. $(8 \cdot 4) + 12$ _____

3. $2 \cdot (3 + 5)$ _____

4. $8 \cdot (4 + 2)$ _____

5. $(4 \cdot 6) - 2$ _____

6. $(7 \cdot 6) - 4$ _____

7. $4 \cdot (6 - 2)$ _____

8. $7 \cdot (6 - 4)$ _____

9. $(28 \div 4) + 3$ _____

10. $(35 \div 5) + 2$ _____

11. $28 \div (4 + 3)$ _____

12. $35 \div (5 + 2)$ _____

13. $9 - (3 \cdot 2)$ _____

14. $17 - (5 \cdot 3)$ _____

15. $(5 - 3) \cdot 2$ _____

16. $(17 - 5) \cdot 3$ _____

Place parentheses to make each statement true.

17. $10 \cdot (2 + 3) = 50$

18. $17 \cdot 3 + 6 = 57$

19. $10 \cdot 2 + 3 = 23$

20. $17 \cdot 3 + 6 = 153$

21. $19 \cdot 2 + 3 = 41$

22. $72 \div 12 \div 2 = 3$

23. $19 \cdot 2 + 3 = 95$

24. $72 \div 12 \div 2 = 12$

25. $56 \div 7 \div 2 = 4$

26. $100 \div 10 \div 10 = 100$

27. $4 \cdot 8 - 8 = 0$

28. $36 \div 3 + 8 = 20$

29. $26 \div 13 - 2 = 0$

30. $26 \cdot 4 - 4 = 0$

31. $41 - 35 \div 6 = 1$

32. $52 - 7 \div 9 = 5$

Inserting Parentheses

Name _____

Date _____ Period _____

Simplify.

1. $(4 \cdot 7) + 8$ _36_

2. $(9 \cdot 3) + 15$ _____

3. $4 \cdot (7 + 8)$ _____

4. $9 \cdot (3 + 15)$ _____

5. $(5 \cdot 4) - 3$ _____

6. $(9 \cdot 5) - 3$ _____

7. $5 \cdot (4 - 3)$ _____

8. $9 \cdot (5 - 3)$ _____

9. $(77 \div 7) + 4$ _____

10. $(104 \div 8) + 5$ _____

11. $77 \div (7 + 4)$ _____

12. $104 \div (8 + 5)$ _____

13. $23 - (4 \cdot 5)$ _____

14. $34 - (4 \cdot 6)$ _____

15. $(23 - 4) \cdot 5$ _____

16. $(34 - 4) \cdot 6$ _____

Place parentheses to make each statement true.

17. $19 \cdot (5 + 2) = 133$

18. $24 \cdot 8 + 5 = 197$

19. $19 \cdot 5 + 2 = 97$

20. $24 \cdot 8 + 5 = 312$

21. $35 \cdot 7 + 9 = 254$

22. $200 \div 4 \div 2 = 25$

23. $35 \cdot 7 + 9 = 560$

24. $100 \div 4 \div 2 = 50$

25. $63 \div 7 \div 3 = 3$

26. $250 \div 10 \div 5 = 125$

27. $6 \cdot 3 - 12 = 6$

28. $49 \div 7 + 8 = 15$

29. $52 \div 26 + 2 = 4$

30. $99 - 33 \div 3 = 88$

31. $84 \div 6 \div 2 = 28$

32. $52 \div 26 \div 2 = 1$

Grouping Symbols

Name _____

Date _____ Period _____

Simplify.

1. $(72 \div 9) - (3 \cdot 2)$ _2_   **2.** $(85 \div 5) - (3 \cdot 5)$ _____

3. $[(72 \div 9) - 3] \cdot 2$ _____   **4.** $[(85 \div 5) - 3] \cdot 5$ _____

5. $(96 \div 6) + (2 \cdot 3)$ _____   **6.** $(125 \div 5) + (4 \cdot 7)$ _____

7. $[(96 \div 6) + 2] \cdot 3$ _____   **8.** $[(125 \div 5) + 4] \cdot 7$ _____

9. $(2 \cdot 4) + (16 \div 2)$ _____   **10.** $(3 \cdot 6) + (15 \div 3)$ _____

11. $[(2 \cdot 4) + 16] \div 2$ _____   **12.** $[(3 \cdot 6) + 15] \div 3$ _____

13. $(160 \div 10) - (2 \cdot 4)$ _____   **14.** $(125 \div 5) - (3 \cdot 7)$ _____

15. $[(160 \div 10) - 2] \cdot 4$ _____   **16.** $[(125 \div 5) - 3] \cdot 7$ _____

17. $(144 \div 12) - (8 \div 2)$ _____   **18.** $(108 \div 6) - (10 \div 2)$ _____

19. $[(144 \div 12) - 8] \div 2$ _____   **20.** $[(108 \div 6) - 10] \div 2$ _____

21. $(288 \div 12) - (9 \div 3)$ _____   **22.** $(450 \div 15) - (30 \div 5)$ _____

23. $[(288 \div 12) - 9] \div 3$ _____   **24.** $[(450 \div 15) - 30] \div 5$ _____

25. $(3 \cdot 8) + (11 \cdot 6)$ _____   **26.** $(9 \cdot 5) + (13 \cdot 7)$ _____

27. $[(3 \cdot 8) + 11)] \cdot 6$ _____   **28.** $[(9 \cdot 5) + 13] \cdot 7$ _____

29. $3 \cdot [(8 + 11) \cdot 6]$ _____   **30.** $9 \cdot [(5 + 13) \cdot 7]$ _____

31. $3 \cdot [8 + (11 \cdot 6)]$ _____   **32.** $9 \cdot [15 + (13 \cdot 7)]$ _____

Grouping Symbols

Name _____

Date _____ Period _____

Simplify.

1. $(54 \div 6) - (3 \cdot 2)$ *3*

2. $(75 \div 3) - (5 \cdot 2)$ _____

3. $[(54 \div 6) - 3] \cdot 2$ _____

4. $[(75 \div 3) - 5] \cdot 2$ _____

5. $(84 \div 7) + (4 \cdot 5)$ _____

6. $(140 \div 4) + (2 \cdot 6)$ _____

7. $[(84 \div 7) + 4] \cdot 5$ _____

8. $[(140 \div 4) + 2] \cdot 6$ _____

9. $(9 \cdot 5) + (24 \div 3)$ _____

10. $(7 \cdot 8) + (28 \div 4)$ _____

11. $[(9 \cdot 5) + 24] \div 3$ _____

12. $[(7 \cdot 8) + 28] \div 4$ _____

13. $(16 \cdot 8) - (2 \cdot 4)$ _____

14. $(17 \cdot 3) - (6 \cdot 5)$ _____

15. $[(16 \cdot 8) - 2] \cdot 4$ _____

16. $[(17 \cdot 3) - 6] \cdot 5$ _____

17. $(7 \cdot 54) - (12 \div 6)$ _____

18. $(4 \cdot 18) - (9 \div 3)$ _____

19. $[(7 \cdot 54) - 12] \div 6$ _____

20. $[(4 \cdot 18) - 9] \div 3$ _____

21. $(14 \cdot 108) - (24 \div 12)$ _____

22. $(17 \cdot 117) - (27 \div 9)$ _____

23. $[(14 \cdot 108) - 24] \div 12$ _____

24. $[(17 \cdot 117) - 27] \div 9$ _____

25. $(120 \div 8) + (4 \div 2)$ _____

26. $(180 \div 2) + (12 \div 3)$ _____

27. $[(120 \div 8) + 4] \div 2$ _____

28. $[(180 \div 2) + 12] \div 3$ _____

29. $120 \div [8 + (4 \div 2)]$ _____

30. $180 \div [2 + (12 \div 3)]$ _____

31. $120 \div [(8 + 4) \div 2]$ _____

32. $180 \div [(2 + 12) \div 3]$ _____

Directed Distance

Name _____

Date _____ Period _____

Positive and negative directions are shown on the number line below. Tell the direction from the first number to the second and how many spaces apart.

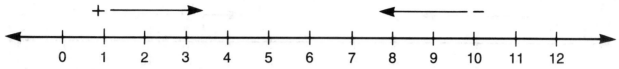

1. 3, 7   ___+___ ___4___   **2.** 10, 1   _____ _____

3. 6, 9   _____ _____   **4.** 11, 8   _____ _____

5. 8, 5   _____ _____   **6.** 2, 12   _____ _____

7. 0, 10   _____ _____   **8.** 10, 0   _____ _____

9. 20, 15   _____ _____   **10.** 25, 13   _____ _____

State the *directed* distance from the first number to the second.

11. 7, 9   _positive_   **12.** 14, 8   _____

13. 2, 10   _____   **14.** 18, 8   _____

15. 9, 9   _____   **16.** 13, 2   _____

17. 4, 15   _____   **18.** 11, 16   _____

19. 17, 7   _____   **20.** 11, 3   _____

21. 8, 17   _____   **22.** 15, 9   _____

Write < or > in the blank to make a true statement.

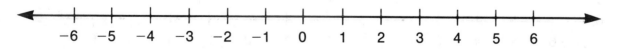

23. −9 _<_ 0   **24.** −3 ___ 8   **25.** 1 ___ −1

26. −7 ___ −8   **27.** −7 ___ 10   **28.** 8 ___ 9

Directed Distance

Name _____

Date _____ Period _____

Positive and negative directions are shown on the number line below. Tell the direction from the first number to the second and how many spaces apart.

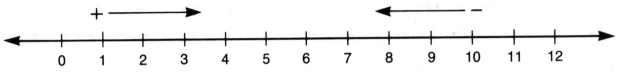

1. 9, 2 _____ − _____ 7 _____   **2.** 5, 12 _____ _____

3. 4, 1 _____ _____   **4.** 7, 0 _____ _____

5. 6, 12 _____ _____   **6.** 10, 3 _____ _____

7. 5, 13 _____ _____   **8.** 0, 15 _____ _____

9. 34, 10 _____ _____   **10.** 18, 29 _____ _____

State the *directed* distance from the first number to the second.

11. 5, 3 *negative*   **12.** 17, 2 _____

13. 4, 18 _____   **14.** 11, 6 _____

15. 18, 21 _____   **16.** 25, 4 _____

17. 8, 33 _____   **18.** 24, 9 _____

19. 22, 6 _____   **20.** 31, 7 _____

21. 14, 23 _____   **22.** 25, 25 _____

Write < or > in the blank to make a true statement.

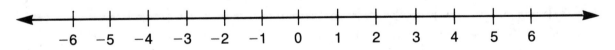

23. −2 < 9   **24.** 7 ___ −10   **25.** −9 ___ −3

26. 8 ___ 6   **27.** 5 ___ −2   **28.** 2 ___ −6

Graphing Integers

Name _____

Date _____ Period _____

Graph each set of integers on the number line provided.

1. {−6, 2, 3, −7, 4, 0, 6, −2}

2. {−4, −1, 4, 5, −3, −5, 8}

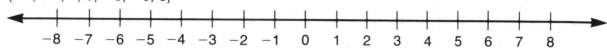

3. {2, 3, 4, −5, 0, −3, −7}

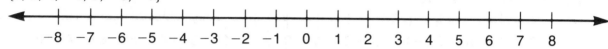

4. {−8, −6, −4, −2, 0, 1, 2, 3}

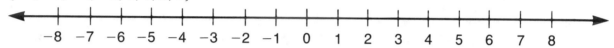

5. {7, 5, 3, 1, −1, −3, −5}

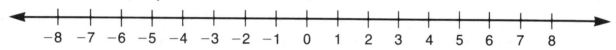

6. {−8, −7, −5, −4, −3, −2, 5}

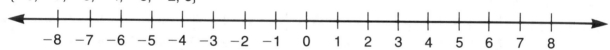

7. {x: −6 < x < 6}

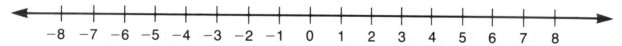

8. {x: x > −3}

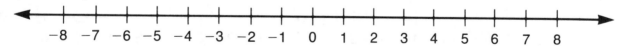

9. {x: x ≤ −1 or x > 5}

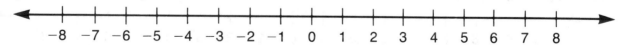

10. {x: x ≤ −2 or x ≥ 4}

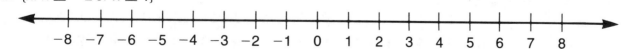

Developing Skills in Algebra   Book A

Graphing Integers

Name _____

Date _____ Period _____

Graph each set of integers on the number line provided.

1. {−4, 1, 0, −5, 2, 3, 5}

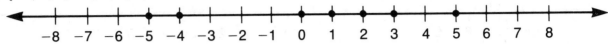

2. {7, −3, 1, 8, −2, −4, 6}

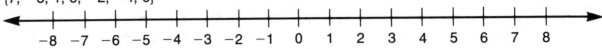

3. {6, −1, 7, −2, 1, −4, −7, 0}

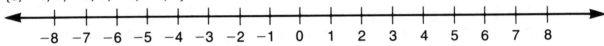

4. {−5, −3, −1, 1, 3, 5, 7}

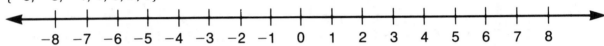

5. {x: $x > 0$}

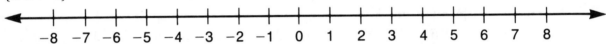

6. {x: $-6 < x \leq 4$}

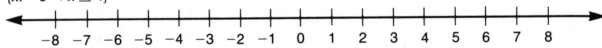

7. {x: $-8 \leq x \leq -2$}

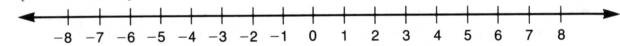

8. {x: $x \leq 0$}

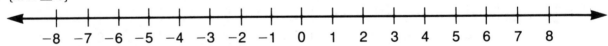

9. {x: $x \geq -5$ or $x < -7$}

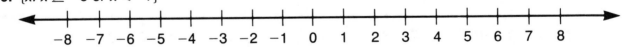

10. {x: $x > 1$ or $x \leq -1$}

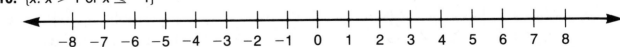

Developing Skills in Algebra   Book A

Absolute Value

Name _____

Date _____ Period _____

Evaluate.

1. $|5|$ _5_   **2.** $|-5|$ _____

3. $|-10|$ _____   **4.** $|12|$ _____

5. $|43|$ _____   **6.** $|-17|$ _____

Simplify.

7. $|-7|+|+3|$ _10_   **8.** $|+15|-|-4|$ _____

9. $|-15|-|-5|$ _____   **10.** $|-29|+|-18|$ _____

11. $|+8|-|-6|$ _____   **12.** $|-19|-|+7|$ _____

13. $|-15|-|+8|$ _____   **14.** $|+27|-|+9|$ _____

15. $7\times|+3|$ _____   **16.** $9\times|-3|$ _____

17. $|-5|\times|+7|$ _____   **18.** $|+7|\times|-7|$ _____

Solve.

19. $|x|=18$ _18, -18_   **20.** $|x|=9$ _____

21. $|x|=22$ _____   **22.** $|x|=-5$ _____

23. $|x|=30$ _____   **24.** $|x|=13$ _____

25. $|x|=44$ _____   **26.** $|x|=29$ _____

27. $|x|=62$ _____   **28.** $|x|=0$ _____

29. $|x|=-11$ _____   **30.** $|x|=11$ _____

Developing Skills in Algebra   Book A

Absolute Value   Name _____

                                        Date _____ Period _____

Evaluate.

1. $|7|$ *7*   **2.** $|-7|$ _____

3. $|-22|$ _____   **4.** $|14|$ _____

5. $|75|$ _____   **6.** $|-63|$ _____

Simplify.

7. $|-9|+|-5|$ *14*   **8.** $|+18|-|-2|$ _____

9. $|-26|-|5|$ _____   **10.** $|35|+|-23|$ _____

11. $|10|-|-8|$ _____   **12.** $|24|-|+21|$ _____

13. $8(|-4|)+2$ _____   **14.** $6(|-5|)+15$ _____

15. $7(|-2|)-4$ _____   **16.** $6(|-8|)-10$ _____

17. $4(|-5|)-|5|$ _____   **18.** $9(|-3|)-|17|$ _____

Solve.

19. $|x|=5$ *5, -5*   **20.** $|x|=12$ _____

21. $|x|=-13$ _____   **22.** $|x|=21$ _____

23. $|x|=0$ _____   **24.** $|x|=25$ _____

25. $|x|=31$ _____   **26.** $|x|=-7$ _____

27. $|x|=99$ _____   **28.** $|x|=17$ _____

29. $|x|=10$ _____   **30.** $|x|=42$ _____

Absolute Value

Name _____

Date _____ Period _____

Graph each set of integers.

1. $\{x: |x| > 4\}$

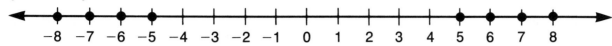

2. $\{x: |x| \leq 3\}$

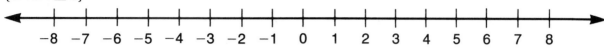

3. $\{x: |x| > 1\}$

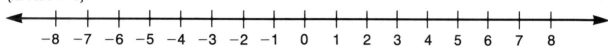

4. $\{x: |x| > 6\}$

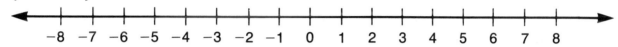

5. $\{x: |x| > 0\}$

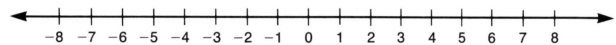

6. $\{x: |x| < 0\}$

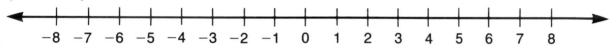

7. $\{x: |x| \leq 5\}$

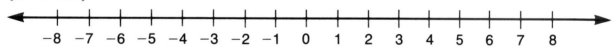

8. $\{x: |x| < -2\}$

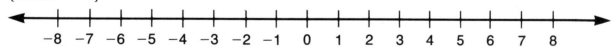

9. $\{x: |x| \leq 1\}$

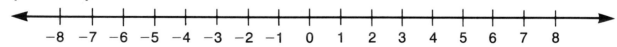

10. $\{x: |x| > 3\}$

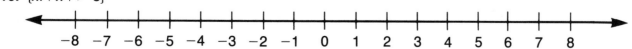

25

Absolute Value

Name _____

Date _____ Period _____

Graph each set of integers.

1. $\{x: |x| \le 2\}$

2. $\{x: |x| \ge 4\}$

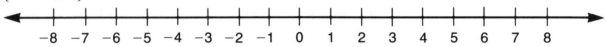

3. $\{x: |x| < -3\}$

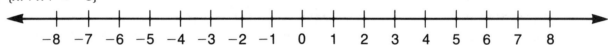

4. $\{x: |x| \le 1\}$

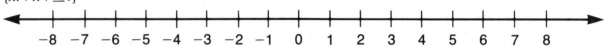

5. $\{x: |x| < 7\}$

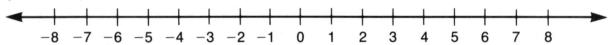

6. $\{x: |x| > 5\}$

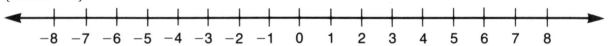

7. $\{x: |x| < 3\}$

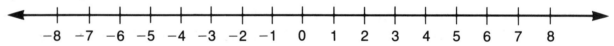

8. $\{x: |x| < 4\}$

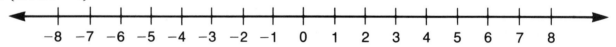

9. $\{x: |x| \ge 0\}$

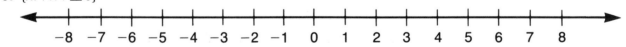

10. $\{x: |x| \ge 2\}$

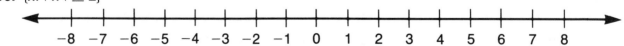

26

Addition of Integers   Name _____

                                        Date _____ Period _____

Use the number line as needed to find the sum of each pair of integers.

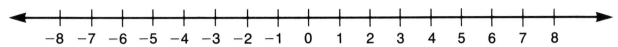

1. 3, −5   _−2_   **2.** 7, −3   _____

3. −4, −1   _____   **4.** 3, −7   _____

5. 3, −3   _____   **6.** −5, 0   _____

7. −6, 7   _____   **8.** −6, −5   _____

9. −6, −7   _____   **10.** −4, −4   _____

11. 6, −7   _____   **12.** 7, −2   _____

13. 6, 7   _____   **14.** −5, 8   _____

15. −2, 5   _____   **16.** −7, −4   _____

Find each sum.

17. −8 + 2   _−6_   **18.** −9 + (−7)   _____

19. 7 + (−3)   _____   **20.** 9 + (−7)   _____

21. −9 + 0   _____   **22.** −15 + 15   _____

23. 3 + 10   _____   **24.** 11 + (−7)   _____

25. −5 + (−1)   _____   **26.** 11 + 7   _____

27. −8 + 8   _____   **28.** −11 + (−7)   _____

29. 3 + (−8)   _____   **30.** −11 + 7   _____

            Developing Skills in Algebra   Book A

Addition of Integers

Name _____

Date _____ Period _____

Use the number line as needed to find the sum of each pair of integers.

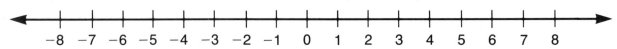

1. 9, −3 ___6___

2. −8, −9 _____

3. −8, −6 _____

4. 9, −7 _____

5. 9, −4 _____

6. −4, −2 _____

7. −2, −2 _____

8. −4, −6 _____

9. 2, −2 _____

10. −3, 5 _____

11. 5, −4 _____

12. −7, −7 _____

13. 8, 7 _____

14. 7, 7 _____

15. −5, 3 _____

16. −8, 8 _____

Find each sum.

17. $-6 + 8$ ___2___

18. $-4 + (-9)$ _____

19. $3 + (-9)$ _____

20. $5 + (-1)$ _____

21. $-7 + (-3)$ _____

22. $13 + (-4)$ _____

23. $-9 + 0$ _____

24. $15 + (-2)$ _____

25. $-9 + (-7)$ _____

26. $-12 + (-11)$ _____

27. $16 + (-10)$ _____

28. $-19 + 4$ _____

29. $9 + (-17)$ _____

30. $-17 + 7$ _____

Developing Skills in Algebra   Book A

Name _____

Date _____ Period _____

Find each sum.

1. $(+7) + (-12) + (15) + (25)$

_____ *35* _____

2. $(-4) + (-6) + (7) + (17)$

_____

3. $(-8) + (25) + (13) + (-11)$

_____

4. $(-3) + (-5) + (-21) + (-35)$

_____

5. $(15) + (-12) + (17) + (-18)$

_____

6. $(28) + (-19) + (-17) + (16)$

_____

7. $(35) + (-22) + (-14) + (17)$

_____

8. $(40) + (-17) + (18) + (-26)$

_____

9. $(-41) + (-32) + (52) + (-15)$

_____

10. $(-8) + (-42) + (-36) + (15)$

_____

11. $(-13) + (-17) + (18) + (35)$

_____

12. $(-8) + (-11) + (18) + (27)$

_____

13. $(-52) + (-17) + (18) + (35)$

_____

14. $(63) + (-41) + (-36) + (12)$

_____

15. $(-14) + (-12) + (23) + (-17)$

_____

16. $(19) + (24) + (43) + (-62)$

_____

17. $(43) + (-51) + (-18) + (27)$

_____

18. $(86) + (-23) + (-15) + (-9)$

_____

19. $(56) + (-9) + (-42) + (-17)$

_____

20. $(18) + (-19) + (27) + (-5)$

_____

Addition of Integers

Name _____

Date _____ Period _____

Find each sum.

1. $(-4) + (-15) + (21) + (16)$

_____ *18* _____

2. $(-8) + (-9) + (5) + (22)$

_____

3. $(-5) + (32) + (18) + (-17)$

_____

4. $(-6) + (-9) + (-29) + (-43)$

_____

5. $(17) + (-18) + (12) + (-11)$

_____

6. $(19) + (-25) + (-12) + (11)$

_____

7. $(47) + (-29) + (-17) + (12)$

_____

8. $(35) + (-19) + (13) + (-33)$

_____

9. $(-49) + (-36) + (45) + (-27)$

_____

10. $(-9) + (-35) + (-53) + (27)$

_____

11. $(-19) + (-12) + (26) + (47)$

_____

12. $(-27) + (-34) + (25) + (-37)$

_____

13. $(47) + (-28) + (32) + (-47)$

_____

14. $(-57) + (-47) + (52) + (-31)$

_____

15. $(35) + (-34) + (-53) + (-41)$

_____

16. $(-34) + (-33) + (58) + (49)$

_____

17. $(-63) + (-44) + (47) + (-43)$

_____

18. $(-74) + (-45) + (37) + (-23)$

_____

19. $(-63) + (-7) + (-37) + (17)$

_____

20. $(18) + (19) + (27) + (5)$

_____

Name _____

Date _____ Period _____

Find each sum.

1. $(15) + (-18) + (-9) + (-5)$

_____-17_____

2. $(32) + (27) + (-13) + (34)$

_____

3. $(-9) + (-7) + (-5) + (-35)$

_____

4. $(21) + (-9) + (-21) + (-34)$

_____

5. $(27) + (-37) + (-9) + (-31)$

_____

6. $(17) + (-15) + (-22) + (-6)$

_____

7. $(-7) + (-36) + (-22) + (-9)$

_____

8. $(-5) + (-34) + (-5) + (-25)$

_____

9. $(-51) + (-26) + (55) + (-32)$

_____

10. $(-4) + (-26) + (-64) + (-3)$

_____

11. $(-18) + (32) + (28) + (-33)$

_____

12. $(32) + (41) + (-35) + (-18)$

_____

13. $(25) + (-26) + (-41) + (-27)$

_____

14. $(57) + (-48) + (-43) + (-18)$

_____

15. $(-65) + (-44) + (71) + (-32)$

_____

16. $(-34) + (39) + (-63) + (-50)$

_____

17. $(-76) + (49) + (-36) + (-37)$

_____

18. $(53) + (-78) + (-64) + (-36)$

_____

19. $(54) + (-9) + (-67) + (-27)$

_____

20. $(-18) + (19) + (-59) + (-8)$

_____

Addition of Integers

Name _____

Date _____ Period _____

Find each sum.

1. $(-5) + (-23) + (15) + (22)$

_____9_____

2. $(-8) + (-9) + (-56) + (43)$

_____

3. $(21) + (-5) + (11) + (-27)$

_____

4. $(-8) + (33) + (-45) + (-57)$

_____

5. $(29) + (-67) + (43) + (-21)$

_____

6. $(26) + (-36) + (-57) + (-9)$

_____

7. $(56) + (-76) + (-43) + (49)$

_____

8. $(67) + (-54) + (98) + (-54)$

_____

9. $(-55) + (-66) + (-69) + (32)$

_____

10. $(15) + (-37) + (64) + (78)$

_____

11. $(-38) + (39) + (-58) + (-63)$

_____

12. $(-42) + (39) + (-64) + (-55)$

_____

13. $(-45) + (28) + (-64) + (47)$

_____

14. $(-87) + (-28) + (46) + (-19)$

_____

15. $(-45) + (48) + (-78) + (-42)$

_____

16. $(-39) + (-59) + (63) + (-57)$

_____

17. $(-75) + (-45) + (-35) + (33)$

_____

18. $(-42) + (78) + (-52) + (61)$

_____

19. $(-44) + (99) + (-65) + (-24)$

_____

20. $(58) + (45) + (-94) + (-5)$

_____

Name _____

Date _____ Period _____

Write an integer in the blank to make a true statement.

1. $9 + \underline{\ -4\ } = 5$

2. $-5 + \underline{\hspace{2em}} = 3$

3. $-5 + \underline{\hspace{2em}} = -3$

4. $4 + \underline{\hspace{2em}} = -1$

5. $-8 + \underline{\hspace{2em}} = 4$

6. $\underline{\hspace{2em}} + (-8) = -7$

7. $\underline{\hspace{2em}} + (-7) = 5$

8. $\underline{\hspace{2em}} + 9 = -13$

9. $\underline{\hspace{2em}} + (-3) = -1$

10. $\underline{\hspace{2em}} + (-7) = 3$

11. $\underline{\hspace{2em}} + (-2) = 0$

12. $\underline{\hspace{2em}} + (-4) = 8$

13. $\underline{\hspace{2em}} + (-9) = -13$

14. $\underline{\hspace{2em}} + 5 = -14$

15. $\underline{\hspace{2em}} + (-6) = -4$

16. $-7 + \underline{\hspace{2em}} = -12$

17. $13 + \underline{\hspace{2em}} = -15$

18. $18 + \underline{\hspace{2em}} = -15$

19. $-15 + \underline{\hspace{2em}} = 7$

20. $-16 + \underline{\hspace{2em}} = 0$

21. $-3 + \underline{\hspace{2em}} = -9$

22. $1 + \underline{\hspace{2em}} = -1$

23. $-2 + \underline{\hspace{2em}} = -10$

24. $1 + \underline{\hspace{2em}} = -13$

25. $-5 + \underline{\hspace{2em}} = 6$

26. $-18 + \underline{\hspace{2em}} = -36$

27. $24 + \underline{\hspace{2em}} = 9$

28. $-26 + \underline{\hspace{2em}} = -13$

29. $32 + \underline{\hspace{2em}} = 30$

30. $-27 + \underline{\hspace{2em}} = -35$

31. $-9 + \underline{\hspace{2em}} = 28$

32. $-34 + \underline{\hspace{2em}} = 27$

Addition of Integers

Name _____

Date _____ Period _____

Write an integer in the blank to make a true statement.

1. $7 + \underline{-10} = -3$

2. $12 + \underline{\hspace{1cm}} = 5$

3. $-9 + \underline{\hspace{1cm}} = 8$

4. $8 + \underline{\hspace{1cm}} = 11$

5. $15 + \underline{\hspace{1cm}} = -7$

6. $\underline{\hspace{1cm}} + (-5) = -2$

7. $\underline{\hspace{1cm}} + 12 = -3$

8. $\underline{\hspace{1cm}} + 4 = -17$

9. $\underline{\hspace{1cm}} + (-6) = 17$

10. $\underline{\hspace{1cm}} + 12 = -22$

11. $\underline{\hspace{1cm}} + 16 = -5$

12. $\underline{\hspace{1cm}} + (-9) = 18$

13. $\underline{\hspace{1cm}} + (-7) = 25$

14. $\underline{\hspace{1cm}} + 5 = 0$

15. $23 + \underline{\hspace{1cm}} = 15$

16. $-16 + \underline{\hspace{1cm}} = -17$

17. $-13 + \underline{\hspace{1cm}} = -10$

18. $11 + \underline{\hspace{1cm}} = -17$

19. $21 + \underline{\hspace{1cm}} = -16$

20. $-29 + \underline{\hspace{1cm}} = 13$

21. $-32 + \underline{\hspace{1cm}} = -15$

22. $-19 + \underline{\hspace{1cm}} = 32$

23. $\underline{\hspace{1cm}} + (-17) = 35$

24. $\underline{\hspace{1cm}} + 25 = -26$

25. $\underline{\hspace{1cm}} + 33 = 72$

26. $\underline{\hspace{1cm}} + (-41) = -27$

27. $\underline{\hspace{1cm}} + (-50) = -88$

28. $\underline{\hspace{1cm}} + 32 = -21$

29. $\underline{\hspace{1cm}} + 88 = 101$

30. $\underline{\hspace{1cm}} + (-39) = -57$

31. $\underline{\hspace{1cm}} + (-41) = 36$

32. $\underline{\hspace{1cm}} + (-63) = -27$

Subtraction of Integers

Name _____

Date _____ Period _____

Write each opposite as indicated.

1. $-(-5) =$ _5_

2. $-(13) =$ _____

3. $-(34) =$ _____

4. $-(-44) =$ _____

5. $-(-52) =$ _____

6. $-(81) =$ _____

Complete each subtraction problem by adding the opposite.

7. $17 - 22$ _-5_

8. $25 - 36$ _____

9. $-15 - (-13)$ _____

10. $-35 - (-22)$ _____

11. $28 - (-17)$ _____

12. $37 - (-24)$ _____

13. $-46 - (-52)$ _____

14. $-63 - (-75)$ _____

15. $81 - (-32)$ _____

16. $71 - (-24)$ _____

17. $43 - 42$ _____

18. $57 - 54$ _____

19. $-77 - 36$ _____

20. $-92 - 58$ _____

21. $43 - (-86)$ _____

22. $37 - (-77)$ _____

23. $-15 - (-99)$ _____

24. $-13 - (-69)$ _____

25. $32 - 65$ _____

26. $48 - 82$ _____

27. $-82 - (-35)$ _____

28. $-45 - (-17)$ _____

29. $-43 - 55$ _____

30. $-64 - 73$ _____

31. $-39 - 43$ _____

32. $48 - 69$ _____

Subtraction of Integers

Name _____

Date _____ Period _____

Write each opposite as indicated.

1. $-(-9) = $ __9__

2. $-(17) = $ _____

3. $-(-7) = $ _____

4. $-(-21) = $ _____

5. $-(45) = $ _____

6. $-(-93) = $ _____

Complete each subtraction problem by adding the opposite.

7. $15 - 35$ __−20__

8. $29 - 49$ _____

9. $-26 - (-22)$ _____

10. $47 - (-17)$ _____

11. $43 - (-15)$ _____

12. $22 - (-35)$ _____

13. $-21 - (29)$ _____

14. $-34 - (-51)$ _____

15. $-9 - (-38)$ _____

16. $26 - (-45)$ _____

17. $86 - 55$ _____

18. $72 - 44$ _____

19. $74 - (-21)$ _____

20. $-47 - 23$ _____

21. $24 - (-32)$ _____

22. $93 - 102$ _____

23. $295 - (-51)$ _____

24. $-37 - (-64)$ _____

25. $68 - 79$ _____

26. $56 - 90$ _____

27. $-53 - 52$ _____

28. $-22 - (-66)$ _____

29. $-73 - 22$ _____

30. $-13 - 56$ _____

31. $-23 - (-15)$ _____

32. $48 - (-37)$ _____

Addition and Subtraction of Integers

Name _____

Date _____ Period _____

Write each difference as a sum, then simplify.

1. $13 - (-10)$ $\underline{13 + 10}$ $\underline{23}$ **2.** $-15 - (-5)$ _____ _____

3. $27 - (-11)$ _____ _____   **4.** $-34 - (16)$ _____ _____

5. $-55 - (-22)$ _____ _____   **6.** $72 - (-13)$ _____ _____

7. $75 - (35)$ _____ _____   **8.** $-67 - (24)$ _____ _____

9. $28 - (-38)$ _____ _____   **10.** $68 - (43)$ _____ _____

Rewrite each expression without double signs, then simplify.

11. $-15 + (-10)$ $\underline{-15 - 10}$ $\underline{-25}$ **12.** $33 - (-10)$ _____ _____

13. $-42 - (-17)$ _____ _____   **14.** $-26 + (-13)$ _____ _____

15. $-35 - (-22)$ _____ _____   **16.** $47 + (-15)$ _____ _____

17. $27 + (53)$ _____ _____   **18.** $65 + (72)$ _____ _____

19. $-45 - (-11)$ _____ _____   **20.** $72 - (-23)$ _____ _____

21. $63 - (-72)$ _____ _____   **22.** $41 - (-65)$ _____ _____

23. $-55 + (-27)$ _____ _____   **24.** $-92 + (-29)$ _____ _____

25. $-37 - (55)$ _____ _____   **26.** $-63 - (37)$ _____ _____

27. $-22 - (-37)$ _____ _____   **28.** $-86 - (-47)$ _____ _____

29. $-63 + (-86)$ _____ _____   **30.** $-82 + (-95)$ _____ _____

31. $-26 - (-44)$ _____ _____   **32.** $34 - (43)$ _____ _____

Addition and Subtraction of Integers

Name _____

Date _____ Period _____

Write each difference as a sum, then simplify.

1. $24 - (-32)$ $24 + 32$ 56 **2.** $-11 - (-9)$ _____ ___

3. $33 - (-18)$ _____ ___   **4.** $-26 - (43)$ _____ ___

5. $-26 - (-35)$ _____ ___   **6.** $61 - (-32)$ _____ ___

7. $73 - (41)$ _____ ___   **8.** $-56 - (38)$ _____ ___

9. $32 - (-74)$ _____ ___   **10.** $23 - (61)$ _____ ___

Rewrite each expression without double signs, then simplify.

11. $-33 + (-17)$ $-33 - 17$ -50 **12.** $26 - (-12)$ _____ ___

13. $-67 - (-32)$ _____ ___   **14.** $-14 + (-33)$ _____ ___

15. $-62 - (-15)$ _____ ___   **16.** $24 + (-37)$ _____ ___

17. $42 + (44)$ _____ ___   **18.** $34 + (81)$ _____ ___

19. $-37 - (-14)$ _____ ___   **20.** $91 - (-42)$ _____ ___

21. $55 - (-26)$ _____ ___   **22.** $63 - (-27)$ _____ ___

23. $-31 + (-39)$ _____ ___   **24.** $-43 + (-49)$ _____ ___

25. $-71 - (54)$ _____ ___   **26.** $-19 - (42)$ _____ ___

27. $-30 - (-58)$ _____ ___   **28.** $-26 - (-39)$ _____ ___

29. $-27 + (-93)$ _____ ___   **30.** $-43 + (-68)$ _____ ___

31. $-17 - (-63)$ _____ ___   **32.** $24 - (71)$ _____ ___

Addition and Subtraction of Integers   Name _____

Date _____ Period _____

Rewrite each difference, then simplify.

1. $15 - (-25)$ $15 + 25$ 40 **2.** $-28 - (-43)$ _____ ____

3. $-43 - (42)$ _____ ____   **4.** $27 - (-26)$ _____ ____

5. $-57 - (-58)$ _____ ____   **6.** $26 - (45)$ _____ ____

7. $38 - (-82)$ _____ ____   **8.** $-56 - (91)$ _____ ____

9. $-45 - (85)$ _____ ____   **10.** $48 - (-57)$ _____ ____

Rewrite each expression without double signs, then simplify.

11. $-27 + (-18)$ $-27 - 18$ -45 **12.** $-22 + (-11)$ _____ ____

13. $-15 - (-24)$ _____ ____   **14.** $-12 - (-32)$ _____ ____

15. $18 + (-43)$ _____ ____   **16.** $25 + (-36)$ _____ ____

17. $-35 - (57)$ _____ ____   **18.** $-42 - (62)$ _____ ____

19. $43 - (-82)$ _____ ____   **20.** $54 - (-75)$ _____ ____

21. $-75 + (-43)$ _____ ____   **22.** $-36 + (-59)$ _____ ____

23. $48 - (-82)$ _____ ___   **24.** $37 - (-68)$ _____ ____

25. $-56 - (-21) + (-26)$ _____ ____   **26.** $-39 - (-12) + (-53)$ _____ ____

27. $-26 - (-81) + (-32)$ _____ ____   **28.** $-42 - (75) + (-53)$ _____ ____

29. $-29 + (-81) + (-32)$ _____ ____   **30.** $-32 + (-88) + (-53)$ _____ ____

31. $17 - (46) - (-18)$ _____ ____   **32.** $29 - (32) - (-27)$ _____ ____

33. $-18 - (-58) - (35)$ _____ ____   **34.** $-27 - (-62) - (43)$ _____ ____

35. $42 - (-27) - (46)$ _____ ____   **36.** $65 - (-28) - (82)$ _____ ____

37. $-33 - (-26) + (-76)$ _____ ____   **38.** $-51 - (-32) + (-13)$ _____ ____

39. $85 + (-43) - (51)$ _____ ____   **40.** $96 + (-28) - (-65)$ _____ ____

41. $43 + (-65) + (32)$ _____ ____   **42.** $37 + (-82) + (51)$ _____ ____

43. $51 + (-46) - (-26)$ _____ ____   **44.** $-27 + (-81) - (-35)$ _____ ____

45. $-29 - (-66) - (-28)$ _____ ____   **46.** $-48 - (-82) - (-26)$ _____ ____

---

39   Developing Skills in Algebra   Book A

Addition and Subtraction of Integers

Name _____

Date _____ Period _____

Rewrite each difference, then simplify.

1. $12 - (-36)$ *12 + 36*   *48*   **2.** $25 - (-17)$ _____ ____

3. $15 - (-42)$ _____ ____   **4.** $29 - (-48)$ _____ ____

5. $-35 - (-53)$ _____ ____   **6.** $38 - (-15)$ _____ ____

7. $56 - (-85)$ _____ ____   **8.** $-75 - (83)$ _____ ____

9. $-61 - (92)$ _____ ____   **10.** $-57 - (72)$ _____ ____

Rewrite each expression without double signs, then simplify.

11. $-24 - (-42)$ *−24 + 42*   *18*   **12.** $-35 + (-18)$ _____ ____

13. $-26 - (-42)$ _____ ____   **14.** $-16 - (-39)$ _____ ____

15. $16 + (-51)$ _____ ____   **16.** $32 + (-65)$ _____ ____

17. $-48 - (75)$ _____ ____   **18.** $-51 - (43)$ _____ ____

19. $57 - (-95)$ _____ ____   **20.** $32 - (-81)$ _____ ____

21. $-62 + (-28)$ _____ ____   **22.** $-43 + (-77)$ _____ ____

23. $53 - (-87)$ _____ ____   **24.** $49 - (-91)$ _____ ____

25. $-32 - (-27) + (-32)$ _____ ____   **26.** $-43 - (-16) + (-48)$ _____ ____

27. $-32 - (-27) + (-52)$ _____ ____   **28.** $-63 - (82) + (-15)$ _____ ____

29. $-43 + (-75) + (-21)$ _____ ____   **30.** $-42 + (-16) + (-67)$ _____ ____

31. $26 - (53) - (-21)$ _____ ____   **32.** $35 - (-27) - (-57)$ _____ ____

33. $-28 - (-62) - (43)$ _____ ____   **34.** $-36 - (-42) - (58)$ _____ ____

35. $59 - (-32) - (41)$ _____ ____   **36.** $72 - (-43) - (52)$ _____ ____

37. $-28 - (-37) + (-81)$ _____ ____   **38.** $16 - (-48) + (-24)$ _____ ____

39. $94 + (-52) - (73)$ _____ ____   **40.** $108 + (-16) - (65)$ _____ ____

41. $33 + (-57) + (47)$ _____ ____   **42.** $45 + (-75) + (62)$ _____ ____

43. $-73 + (-82) - (-21)$ _____ ____   **44.** $-16 + (-77) - (-28)$ _____ ____

45. $-43 - (-82) - (-34)$ _____ ____   **46.** $-62 - (-55) - (-34)$ _____ ____

Addition and Subtraction of Integers

Name _____

Date _____ Period _____

Find each sum.

1. $-6 - 5 + 14 - 7 + 2 - 1$ **−3**

2. $-8 + 12 - 19 + 17 - 6 - 12$ _____

3. $5 + 7 - 8 - 16 + 4 - 9$ _____

4. $12 + 8 - 16 - 19 + 14 - 6$ _____

5. $18 - 2 + 17 + 12 - 16$ _____

6. $14 + 9 - 16 - 17 - 21 + 2$ _____

7. $26 - 25 + 14 + 11 - 11$ _____

8. $26 + 32 - 17 - 18 - 6 - 3$ _____

9. $-8 + 14 - 19 + 12 - 15$ _____

10. $9 - 6 + 13 - 15 - 17 + 7$ _____

11. $14 - 3 + 23 - 17 - 9$ _____

12. $25 - 18 - 17 - 16 + 17 + 9$ _____

13. $28 + 32 - 51 - 16 - 24$ _____

14. $-42 + 13 - 15 - 6 + 9 - 5$ _____

15. $-12 + 13 + 26 + 42 - 35$ _____

16. $-9 + 13 - 15 - 27 - 16$ _____

17. $-43 + 17 - 26 + 14 - 7$ _____

18. $-51 + 42 - 16 - 17 - 21$ _____

19. $-9 + 16 - 15 + 21 + 35$ _____

20. $-56 + 48 + 16 - 19 + 12$ _____

21. $45 + 48 - 62 + 11 - 15$ _____

22. $-26 + 32 + 15 - 67 + 14$ _____

23. $-26 + 31 + 42 - 27 - 14$ _____

24. $52 + 26 - 28 - 65 - 63$ _____

25. $23 - 16 + 11 - 12 + 13$ _____

26. $-75 + 81 + 82 - 16 + 17$ _____

27. $43 - 51 - 62 - 18 + 17$ _____

28. $-48 + 29 + 32 - 43 + 16$ _____

29. $26 - 17 - 28 + 43 + 21$ _____

30. $35 + 41 + 16 - 17 - 29$ _____

31. $36 - 16 + 27 - 23 - 46$ _____

32. $48 - 46 - 27 - 26 + 17$ _____

33. $51 + 32 - 43 - 62 - 17$ _____

34. $27 + 32 - 112 + 34 - 16$ _____

35. $124 - 18 - 27 - 82 + 19$ _____

36. $26 - 43 + 19 - 52 + 6 - 9$ _____

37. $-85 + 42 + 75 - 62 - 57$ _____

38. $-23 + 88 + 46 - 75 - 116$ _____

39. $-72 - 63 + 14 + 29 - 16$ _____

40. $-12 + 17 - 18 - 27 - 163$ _____

41. $-28 + 13 - 57 - 82 + 26$ _____

42. $-46 + 29 + 32 - 65 - 82$ _____

43. $-75 + 34 - 26 - 17 + 96$ _____

44. $-102 + 51 + 33 - 26 + 27$ _____

45. $-87 - 82 + 43 + 51 - 116$ _____

46. $95 + 26 - 47 - 53 + 14$ _____

47. $113 + 45 - 37 - 16 + 3$ _____

48. $-83 - 42 + 16 - 25 + 13$ _____

Addition and Subtraction of Integers

Name _____

Date _____ Period _____

Find each sum.

1. $-9 - 3 + 23 - 9 + 5 - 6$ ___/___
2. $-3 + 22 - 15 + 19 - 4 - 25$ _____
3. $9 + 3 - 7 - 14 + 8 - 3$ _____
4. $18 + 9 - 25 - 13 + 17 - 2$ _____
5. $15 - 7 + 19 + 16 - 27$ _____
6. $19 + 3 - 18 - 19 - 32 + 5$ _____
7. $28 - 34 + 23 + 10 - 15$ _____
8. $37 + 42 - 23 - 14 - 8 - 2$ _____
9. $-9 + 13 - 15 + 26 - 19$ _____
10. $2 - 8 + 18 - 21 - 10 + 13$ _____
11. $18 - 7 + 31 - 10 - 8$ _____
12. $36 - 29 - 10 - 15 + 13 + 7$ _____
13. $42 + 35 - 37 - 24 - 28$ _____
14. $-32 + 23 - 35 - 7 + 2 - 1$ _____
15. $-17 + 13 + 31 + 40 - 52$ _____
16. $-7 + 24 - 33 - 63 - 10$ _____
17. $-31 + 26 - 35 + 22 - 9$ _____
18. $-31 + 55 - 13 - 36 - 42$ _____
19. $-4 + 22 - 34 + 32 + 55$ _____
20. $-37 + 29 + 25 - 42 + 16$ _____
21. $37 + 44 - 38 + 42 - 27$ _____
22. $-56 + 43 + 28 - 33 + 28$ _____
23. $-52 + 37 + 73 - 42 - 37$ _____
24. $42 + 37 - 34 - 66 - 53$ _____
25. $33 - 38 + 31 - 22 + 53$ _____
26. $-25 + 73 + 94 - 15 + 26$ _____
27. $72 - 50 - 43 - 25 + 32$ _____
28. $-29 + 34 + 52 - 82 + 37$ _____
29. $42 - 36 - 55 + 38 + 16$ _____
30. $44 + 72 + 29 - 35 - 14$ _____
31. $53 - 37 + 83 - 44 - 67$ _____
32. $49 - 63 - 55 - 32 + 73$ _____
33. $73 + 22 - 54 - 74 - 32$ _____
34. $43 + 71 - 125 + 83 - 27$ _____
35. $102 - 37 - 48 - 53 + 27$ _____
36. $73 - 53 + 64 - 21 + 8 - 2$ _____
37. $-27 + 38 + 44 - 70 - 61$ _____
38. $-37 + 45 + 32 - 81 - 137$ _____
39. $-53 - 49 + 28 + 32 - 44$ _____
40. $-19 + 33 - 42 - 37 - 121$ _____
41. $-34 + 26 - 48 - 91 + 33$ _____
42. $-59 + 35 + 28 - 48 - 35$ _____
43. $-82 + 26 - 44 - 39 + 29$ _____
44. $-133 + 47 + 82 - 47 + 31$ _____
45. $-32 - 55 + 61 + 78 - 103$ _____
46. $46 + 32 - 59 - 80 + 23$ _____
47. $152 + 72 - 43 - 33 + 27$ _____
48. $-29 - 51 + 38 - 42 + 56$ _____

42

Developing Skills in Algebra   Book A

Multiplication of Integers

Name _____

Date _____ Period _____

_____

Find each product.

1. $-7(3)$ $\underline{-21}$

2. $-4(-3)$ _____

3. $-12(-13)$ _____

4. $-11(35)$ _____

5. $6(-11)$ _____

6. $7(-23)$ _____

7. $-14(-27)$ _____

8. $-19(-24)$ _____

9. $16(-22)$ _____

10. $-15(25)$ _____

11. $(-3)(16)(-5)$ _____

12. $(-7)(13)(-12)$ _____

13. $-14(-6)(-15)$ _____

14. $-28(-5)(-22)$ _____

15. $17(-14)(-11)$ _____

16. $29(-16)(-24)$ _____

Simplify.

17. $-15(-2) + (16)(-5)$ $\underline{-50}$

18. $-23(-4) + (22)(-7)$ _____

19. $26(23) + (-11)(-7)$ _____

20. $16(42) + (-13)(-19)$ _____

21. $43(-22) - (-16)(6)$ _____

22. $27(-18) - (-14)(-9)$ _____

23. $-16(-15) - (15)(-8)$ _____

24. $-31(-6) - (13)(-7)$ _____

25. $38(-16) - (11)(-13)$ _____

26. $63(-4) - (32)(-15)$ _____

27. $17(13) + (-8)(45)$ _____

28. $18(12) + (-6)(52)$ _____

29. $25(-13) - (13)(-8)$ _____

30. $43(-22) - 45(-17)$ _____

31. $36(-7) - (18)(-4)$ _____

32. $42(-11) - (17)(-6)$ _____

Multiplication of Integers

Name _____

Date _____ Period _____

Find each product.

1. $-9(5)$ _−45_   **2.** $-8(15)$ _____

3. $-16(-17)$ _____   **4.** $-13(-7)$ _____

5. $-5(-12)$ _____   **6.** $8(-19)$ _____

7. $21(-12)$ _____   **8.** $-14(-22)$ _____

9. $33(-13)$ _____   **10.** $-11(45)$ _____

11. $(-5)(-7)(-3)$ _____   **12.** $(-8)(11)(-16)$ _____

13. $28(-32)(-15)$ _____   **14.** $33(-42)(-21)$ _____

15. $27(43)(-51)$ _____   **16.** $52(41)(-16)$ _____

Simplify.

17. $-11(-3) + (14)(-2)$ _5_   **18.** $-21(-5) + (13)(-6)$ _____

19. $14(-9) + (-22)(-9)$ _____   **20.** $17(23) + (-16)(-17)$ _____

21. $55(-11) - (-14)(2)$ _____   **22.** $31(-12) - (-15)(-7)$ _____

23. $33(14) + (-7)(-9)$ _____   **24.** $53(12) + (-6)(-10)$ _____

25. $57(-22) - (13)(-32)$ _____   **26.** $28(-17) - (15)(-29)$ _____

27. $28(13) - (-7)(8)$ _____   **28.** $45(11) + (-6)(13)$ _____

29. $-45(-22) + (-11)(-7)$ _____   **30.** $-16(-34) + (-15)(-9)$ _____

31. $42(-11) - (17)(-22)$ _____   **32.** $28(-21) - (14)(-15)$ _____

    44   Developing Skills in Algebra   Book A

Evaluating Variable Expressions

Evaluate if $a = 3$, $b = -2$, $c = 7$, $d = -1$, and $e = 0$.

1. abc _−42_

2. cde _____

3. $ab + cd$ _____

4. $cd + ac$ _____

5. $ac - de$ _____

6. $cd - ac$ _____

7. $ac + de - bc$ _____

8. $ab + cd + bc$ _____

9. $ad - bc - 3$ _____

10. $de - ab - 7$ _____

11. $ac - 5b + 4a$ _____

12. $bc - 8a + 5b$ _____

13. $bd - 7 + abc$ _____

14. $ad - 11 + 7ab$ _____

15. $(-a)(-b) + bc$ _____

16. $(-c)(-d) + ac$ _____

17. $ab + 3ac - 6bd$ _____

18. $cd - 8bc - 2ad$ _____

19. $|a| + |b| + |c|$ _____

20. $|c| + |d| + |e|$ _____

21. $|a| - |b| - |c|$ _____

22. $|c| - |d| - |e|$ _____

23. $5 + |ab| + |ac|$ _____

24. $8 + |ac| + |bd|$ _____

25. $-4ad - 8bc$ _____

26. $-8bc - 2ad$ _____

27. $14acd + 12ab$ _____

28. $19ad + 21abc$ _____

29. $-22acd + 14ab$ _____

30. $-17ad + 23abc$ _____

31. $-a + bc + 22$ _____

32. $-b + ac + 34$ _____

33. $-5c + 4bd - 3a$ _____

34. $-4b + 10cd - 7a$ _____

Evaluating Variable Expressions   Name _____

Date _____ Period _____

Evaluate if $a = 5$, $b = -3$, $c = 8$, $d = -1$, and $e = 0$.

1. bcd ___*24*___   **2.** acd _____

3. $ac + bc$ _____   **4.** $bd + ab$ _____

5. $ac - bd$ _____   **6.** $bc - ad$ _____

7. $bc + bd - ce$ _____   **8.** $ad + bd - cd$ _____

9. $25 - ac$ _____   **10.** $35 - ad$ _____

11. $4bd + 3ac - ad$ _____   **12.** $3cd - 5bc + bd$ _____

13. $6(-a)(-c)(d)$ _____   **14.** $-8(-b)(-d)(e)$ _____

15. $10a - bcd$ _____   **16.** $15b - acd$ _____

17. $|a| + |b| + |c|$ _____   **18.** $|c| + |d| + |e|$ _____

19. $|ab| + |bc|$ _____   **20.** $|ad| - |abc|$ _____

21. $3|ad| - 5|b|$ _____   **22.** $4|bc| + 10|d|$ _____

23. $|abd| + |acd|$ _____   **24.** $|bcd| - |abc|$ _____

25. $-7bc - 10ad$ _____   **26.** $-11ac - 7bc$ _____

27. $9abd + 7ac$ _____   **28.** $21bc + 13ad$ _____

29. $-32abc + 12bd$ _____   **30.** $-25bcd + 32ad$ _____

31. $-b + ac + 41$ _____   **32.** $-c + bd + 27$ _____

33. $-7a + 2bc - 4d$ _____   **34.** $-9b + 7cd - 8a$ _____

46   Developing Skills in Algebra   Book A

Reciprocals

Name _____

Date _____ Period _____

Write the reciprocal of each integer.

1. -5 $-\frac{1}{5}$

2. 6 _____

3. -12 _____

4. 15 _____

Rewrite each quotient as the product of the dividend and the reciprocal of the divisor, then simplify.

5. $45 \div 15$ $45 \times \frac{1}{15}$ 3

6. $-91 \div 13$ _____ _____

7. $56 \div (-14)$ _____ _____

8. $-105 \div 21$ _____ _____

9. $150 \div (-25)$ _____ _____

10. $-169 \div (-13)$ _____ _____

11. $-200 \div (-8)$ _____ _____

12. $272 \div (-16)$ _____ _____

Rewrite each product as one fraction, then simplify.

13. $\frac{1}{8}(208)$ $\frac{208}{8}$ 26

14. $-\frac{1}{16}(752)$ _____ _____

15. $\frac{1}{25}(-900)$ _____ _____

16. $-\frac{1}{14}(742)$ _____ _____

17. $-\frac{1}{27}(432)$ _____ _____

18. $\frac{1}{29}(1305)$ _____ _____

Write the reciprocal of each rational number.

19. $\frac{4}{5}$ $\frac{5}{4}$

20. $-\frac{2}{3}$ _____

21. $-\frac{8}{7}$ _____

22. $\frac{9}{10}$ _____

Simplify.

23. $-75 \div \left(-\frac{5}{8}\right)$ 120

24. $-48 \div \left(\frac{2}{3}\right)$ _____

25. $-121 \div \left(\frac{11}{5}\right)$ _____

26. $105 \div \left(-\frac{7}{15}\right)$ _____

47

Developing Skills in Algebra   Book A

Reciprocals

Name _____

Date _____ Period _____

Write the reciprocal of each integer.

1. 25 $\frac{1}{25}$ _____

2. -37 _____

3. 105   _____

4. 0   _____

Rewrite each quotient as the product of the dividend and the reciprocal of the divisor, then simplify.

5. $378 \div 14$ $378 \times \frac{1}{14}$ 27

6. $-286 \div 13$ _____ _____

7. $187 \div (-11)$ _____ _____

8. $-133 \div (-19)$ _____ _____

9. $207 \div (-9)$ _____ _____

10. $-315 \div (-21)$ _____ _____

11. $-400 \div (16)$ _____ _____

12. $336 \div (-21)$ _____ _____

Rewrite each product as one fraction, then simplify.

13. $\frac{1}{7}(203)$ $\frac{203}{7}$ 29

14. $-\frac{1}{15}(360)$ _____ _____

15. $\frac{1}{35}(-595)$ _____ _____

16. $-\frac{1}{13}(286)$ _____ _____

17. $-\frac{1}{33}(561)$ _____ _____

18. $\frac{1}{39}(1131)$ _____ _____

Write the reciprocal of each rational number.

19. $\frac{7}{3}$ $\frac{3}{7}$

20. $-\frac{2}{9}$ _____

21. $-\frac{17}{18}$ _____

22. $\frac{21}{29}$ _____

Simplify.

23. $-48 \div \left(-\frac{4}{5}\right)$ 60

24. $-39 \div \left(\frac{3}{8}\right)$ _____

25. $-169 \div \left(\frac{13}{5}\right)$ _____

26. $125 \div \left(-\frac{5}{11}\right)$ _____

Developing Skills in Algebra   Book A

Name _____

Date _____ Period _____

Simplify.

1. $48\left(-\dfrac{1}{8}\right)\left(-\dfrac{1}{2}\right)$ ____3____

2. $-54\left(\dfrac{7}{9}\right)\left(-\dfrac{2}{3}\right)$ _____

3. $-32\left(-\dfrac{3}{4}\right)\left(\dfrac{7}{8}\right)$ _____

4. $\left(\dfrac{3}{4}\right)\left(-\dfrac{5}{2}\right) \div 60$ _____

5. $\left(\dfrac{5}{2}\right)\left(-\dfrac{3}{2}\right) \div 45$ _____

6. $-40\left(-\dfrac{3}{5}\right)\left(-\dfrac{3}{4}\right)$ _____

7. $\left(\dfrac{3}{5}\right)\left(-\dfrac{8}{7}\right) \div 72$ _____

8. $\left(\dfrac{6}{7}\right)\left(-\dfrac{5}{8}\right) \div 45$ _____

9. $48\left(-\dfrac{5}{8}\right) \div \left(\dfrac{3}{7}\right)$ _____

10. $-91\left(-\dfrac{4}{7}\right) \div 92$ _____

Evaluate if $a = 3$, $b = 12$, $c = -5$, $d = -15$ and $e = 4$.

11. $\dfrac{ab}{c}$ $-\dfrac{36}{5}$ or $-7\dfrac{1}{5}$

12. $\dfrac{de}{b}$ _____

13. $\dfrac{ac}{d}$ _____

14. $\dfrac{ce}{b}$ _____

15. $\dfrac{bc}{a} + \dfrac{de}{c}$ _____

16. $\dfrac{ad}{c} + \dfrac{ae}{b}$ _____

17. $\dfrac{b}{ae} - \dfrac{d}{ac}$ _____

18. $\dfrac{bc}{d} - \dfrac{be}{a}$ _____

19. $\dfrac{ab}{de} \div \dfrac{bc}{ae}$ _____

20. $\dfrac{cd}{ac} \div \dfrac{be}{ac}$ _____

21. $\dfrac{c}{de} \cdot \dfrac{a}{bc}$ _____

22. $\dfrac{b}{ac} \cdot \dfrac{c}{de}$ _____

23. $\dfrac{c}{ba} \div \dfrac{d}{ae} + \dfrac{a}{c}$ _____

24. $\dfrac{c}{de} \div \dfrac{c}{be} + \dfrac{a}{e}$ _____

25. $\dfrac{ac}{7} \cdot \dfrac{14}{2d} - \dfrac{a}{e}$ _____

26. $\dfrac{20}{ae} \cdot \dfrac{45}{ce} - \dfrac{c}{3}$ _____

Operations With Numbers

Name _____

Date _____ Period _____

Simplify.

1. $30\left(-\dfrac{1}{3}\right)\left(-\dfrac{1}{2}\right)$ ___5___ **2.** $-72\left(\dfrac{3}{4}\right)\left(-\dfrac{5}{6}\right)$ _____

3. $-56\left(-\dfrac{3}{4}\right)\left(\dfrac{3}{7}\right)$ _____ **4.** $\left(\dfrac{5}{8}\right)\left(-\dfrac{3}{4}\right)\div 30$ _____

5. $\left(\dfrac{7}{2}\right)\left(-\dfrac{3}{5}\right)\div 42$ _____ **6.** $-49\left(-\dfrac{3}{7}\right)\left(-\dfrac{2}{3}\right)$ _____

7. $\left(\dfrac{5}{8}\right)\left(-\dfrac{4}{3}\right)\div 40$ _____ **8.** $\left(\dfrac{5}{7}\right)\left(-\dfrac{5}{8}\right)\div 25$ _____

9. $10\left(-\dfrac{3}{4}\right)\div\left(\dfrac{3}{8}\right)$ _____ **10.** $-87\left(-\dfrac{4}{9}\right)\div 42$ _____

Evaluate if $a = 6$, $b = 16$, $c = -4$, $d = -12$ and $e = -5$.

11. $\dfrac{ad}{c}$ ___18___ **12.** $\dfrac{ad}{b}$ _____

13. $\dfrac{bc}{d}$ _____ **14.** $\dfrac{cb}{d}$ _____

15. $\dfrac{ba}{c} + \dfrac{ae}{d}$ _____ **16.** $\dfrac{ac}{d} + \dfrac{be}{c}$ _____

17. $\dfrac{d}{ab} - \dfrac{a}{b}$ _____ **18.** $\dfrac{be}{c} - \dfrac{ab}{d}$ _____

19. $\dfrac{bc}{ce} \div \dfrac{ac}{ae}$ _____ **20.** $\dfrac{ad}{ac} \div \dfrac{ab}{ce}$ _____

21. $\dfrac{a}{de} \cdot \dfrac{c}{be}$ _____ **22.** $\dfrac{d}{bc} \cdot \dfrac{ce}{a}$ _____

23. $\dfrac{d}{ce} \div \dfrac{a}{be} + \dfrac{a}{c}$ _____ **24.** $\dfrac{a}{bc} \div \dfrac{c}{ba} + \dfrac{a}{e}$ _____

25. $\dfrac{bc}{9} \cdot \dfrac{18}{2d} - \dfrac{c}{a}$ _____ **26.** $\dfrac{22}{be} \cdot \dfrac{15}{11a} - \dfrac{3}{c}$ _____

Number Properties

Name _____

Date _____ Period _____

A. Closure for Addition
B. Commutative for Addition
C. Associative for Addition
D. Identity for Addition
E. Inverse for Addition

F. Closure for Multiplication
G. Commutative for Multiplication
H. Associative for Multiplication
I. Identity for Multiplication
J. Inverse for Multiplication

K. Distributive for Multiplication over Addition

Use the appropriate letter to name the property illustrated. (Assume that variables represent real numbers.)

1. $3 + (5 + 7) = (3 + 5) + 7$ _C_

2. $16 + 27 = 27 + 16$ ____

3. $73 \cdot 86 = 86 \cdot 73$ ____

4. $12 + 0 = 12$ ____

5. $461 \cdot 1 = 461$ ____

6. $326 \cdot 1 = 1 \cdot 326$ ____

7. $x + (y + 5) = (x + y) + 5$ ____

8. $73 \cdot 1 = 73$ ____

9. $(m + n)$ is a real number   ____

10. $a - 3 + b = a + b - 3$ ____

11. $x + (-x) = 0$ ____

12. mn is a real number   ____

13. $73 \cdot 2 = 2 \cdot 73$ ____

14. $b + 3 = 3 + b$ ____

15. $4(7 + 3) = 4 \cdot 7 + 4 \cdot 3$ ____

16. $5(7 + 2) = (7 + 2)5$ ____

17. $7 = 7 + 0$ ____

18. $5(7 + 2) = 5 \cdot 7 + 5 \cdot 2$ ____

19. $13 \cdot 4 \cdot 10 = 13 \cdot 10 \cdot 4$ ____

20. $8 + a + 0 = 8 + a$ ____

21. $(27 + e) + f = (e + 27) + f$ ____

22. $7\left(\dfrac{1}{7}\right) = 1$ ____

Number Properties

Name _____

Date _____ Period _____

A. Closure for Addition
B. Commutative for Addition
C. Associative for Addition
D. Identity for Addition
E. Inverse for Addition

F. Closure for Multiplication
G. Commutative for Multiplication
H. Associative for Multiplication
I. Identity for Multiplication
J. Inverse for Multiplication

K. Distributive for Multiplication over Addition

Use the appropriate letter to name the property illustrated. (Assume that variables represent real numbers.)

1. $8 \cdot 1 = 8$ _____ *I*

2. $7 \cdot 3 = 3 \cdot 7$ _____

3. $(9 + 4) + 6 = 9 + (4 + 6)$ _____

4. $a(b + c) = ab + ac$ _____

5. $8(c + d) = 8(d + c)$ _____

6. $mn + mt = m(n + t)$ _____

7. $8(c + d) = (c + d)8$ _____

8. $4 + (-4) = 0$ _____

9. $4 + 0 = 4$ _____

10. $(a + c)$ is a real number _____

11. $\left(\dfrac{1}{6}\right)(6) = 1$ _____

12. $x \cdot 1 = x$ _____

13. $4 + 7 + x = 7 + 4 + x$ _____

14. $(4 + 7) + x = 4 + (7 + x)$ _____

15. $3 + a = a + 3$ _____

16. $xyz = yxz$ _____

17. ab is a real number _____

18. $35 + 0 = 35$ _____

19. $2 \cdot 5 + 2 \cdot 9 = 2(5 + 9)$ _____

20. $(a + b) \cdot 1 = a + b$ _____

21. $(a + b)7 = 7(a + b)$ _____

22. $6 + (-6) = 0$ _____

Developing Skills in Algebra   Book A

Using Number Properties

Name _____

Date _____ Period _____

Rewrite using the distributive property. Simplify where possible.

1. $4(x+y)$ $4x + 4y$ **2.** $8(3m+4n)$ _____

3. $(2x+3y)7$ _____   **4.** $\frac{1}{2}(6r+10s)$ _____

5. $\frac{3}{4}(12x+16y)$ _____   **6.** $(54+10a)5$ _____

7. $(16+13x)10$ _____   **8.** $(14+7a)\frac{1}{7}$ _____

9. $a(3b+7)$ _____   **10.** $m(2n+15)$ _____

Rewrite using the distributive property. Simplify where possible.

11. $7a+7b$ $7(a+b)$ **12.** $8x+8y$ _____

13. $10c+5d$ _____   **14.** $20m+15n$ _____

15. $20x+x$ _____   **16.** $25x+9x$ _____

17. $12a+16a$ _____   **18.** $26m+18m$ _____

19. $4+4t$ _____   **20.** $9+9x$ _____

Simplify using the commutative and associative properties of multiplication.

21. $2a(7b)$ $14\,ab$ **22.** $-3bc(5m)$ _____

23. $5xy(-2x)(-3y)$ _____   **24.** $7a(-4ab)(2a)$ _____

25. $a(-13b)(22ab)$ _____   **26.** $-cd(5c)(-7cd)$ _____

27. $-15a(4b)(2bc)$ _____   **28.** $7x(-9xy)(-8y)$ _____

Name _____

Date _____ Period _____

Rewrite using the distributive property. Simplify where possible.

1. $5(a + b)$ $5a + 5b$

2. $9(2r + 7s)$ _____

3. $(5c + 2d)(-4)$ _____

4. $\frac{3}{4}(8x + 12y)$ _____

5. $\frac{2}{3}(15x + 21y)$ _____

6. $(17 + 13m)(-3)$ _____

7. $(11 - 9z)13$ _____

8. $(39 - 13c)\frac{1}{13}$ _____

9. $x(5y + 2z)$ _____

10. $m(2n + 15)$ _____

Rewrite using the distributive property. Simplify where possible.

11. $9x + 9y$ $9(x + y)$

12. $5a + 5b$ _____

13. $12c - 8d$ _____

14. $30m - 15n$ _____

15. $15x + 7x$ _____

16. $17r + 12r$ _____

17. $18a + 24a$ _____

18. $15c + 12c$ _____

19. $9 - 9z$ _____

20. $13 - 13x$ _____

Simplify using the commutative and associative properties of multiplication.

21. $7a(-10bc)$ $-70abc$

22. $-3ab(2d)(-5)$ _____

23. $-8m(2n)(4mn)$ _____

24. $7x(-3xy)(5y)$ _____

25. $2c(-4abc)(8ab)$ _____

26. $-10d(6cd)(-2d)$ _____

27. $6xy(-4x)(2xy)$ _____

28. $12mn(-8m)(6mn)$ _____

Combining Like Terms

Name _____

Date _____ Period _____

Simplify by combining like terms.

1. $2a + 15a + 3a$ _20a_

2. $7x + 19x + 13x$ _____

3. $5y - 13y + 10y$ _____

4. $6c - 22c + 12c$ _____

5. $35x + 55x + 4$ _____

6. $37y + 10 + 15y$ _____

7. $26ab + 14ab$ _____

8. $12mn + 25mn$ _____

9. $3abc - 22abc$ _____

10. $15rst - 33rst$ _____

11. $7a + 6c + 9a - 15c$ _____

12. $14x + 7y - 19x + 15y$ _____

13. $6c - 9c + 5 + 10c$ _____

14. $7r + 8 + 10r - 19r$ _____

15. $21x + 14 - 15x + 22$ _____

16. $35n + 41 - 19n + 35$ _____

17. $3xy + 3x - 5xy + 4x$ _____

18. $9bc + 10c - 21c + 13bc$ _____

19. $4x^2y + 2x^2y - 5x^2y$ _____

20. $8x^3 - 7x^3 + 16x^3$ _____

21. $15x^2y - 7x^2y + 3$ _____

22. $-14a^2b + 25a^2b - 7$ _____

23. $4x^2 + 2x - 3x^2 + 4x$ _____

24. $5m^3 + 2m^2 - 7m^3 - 8m$ _____

25. $7xy + 4yz - 10yz$ _____

26. $23rs + 11st - 25st$ _____

27. $7x^2 + 2xy - 7xy + 4y^2$ _____

28. $a^2 + 7ab - 10ab + b^2$ _____

29. $-4a^2b + 7 + 10a^2b$ _____

30. $15c^3d + 18c^3d - 9$ _____

31. $8x^2 - 14x + 10x^2$ _____

32. $9y^3 - 18y^2 + 16y^2$ _____

Developing Skills in Algebra   Book A

Combining Like Terms

Name _____

Date _____ Period _____

Simplify by combining like terms.

1. $4x + 13x + 9x$ $26x$ **2.** $2c + 15c + 21c$ _____

3. $9y - 21y + 14y$ _____   **4.** $7z - 19z + 23z$ _____

5. $43a + 32a + 25$ _____   **6.** $26r + 12 + 19r$ _____

7. $32xy - 19xy$ _____   **8.** $16cd - 31cd$ _____

9. $7xyz - 19xyz$ _____   **10.** $23cde - 12cde$ _____

11. $8x - 7y + 5x - 19y$ _____   **12.** $18c - 9d - 22c + 14d$ _____

13. $9a - 13a + 7 - 22a$ _____   **14.** $5m + 3 + 19m - 22m$ _____

15. $32c - 23 - 14c - 31$ _____   **16.** $42x + 33 - 12x - 42$ _____

17. $9ab - 7b + 8ab + 3b$ _____   **18.** $8rs - 17s - 19s - 16rs$ _____

19. $7x^2y - 9x^2y - 2x^2y$ _____   **20.** $6a^3 - 9a^3 + 25a^3$ _____

21. $22m^2n + 3m^2n - 15$ _____   **22.** $-21c^2d - 31c^2d + 9$ _____

23. $55a^2 - b + 11a^2$ _____   **24.** $17x^3 - 11y^2 - 14x^3$ _____

25. $r^2s + r^2s + r^2s$ _____   **26.** $ab^3 + ab^3 + ab^3$ _____

27. $6xy^2 - 15xy^2 + 10x^2y$ _____   **28.** $19a^2b - 22ab^2 + 15ab^2$ _____

29. $45x^2 - 22y + 11x^2$ _____   **30.** $24a^2 + 16b^2 - 17a^2$ _____

31. $-25abc^2 + 44abc^2$ _____   **32.** $-57x^2y^2z - 88x^2y^2z$ _____

Checking for Solutions

A domain is given for each equation. Circle all solutions in the domain. If there are no solutions in the domain, cross it out and write ∅.

		DOMAIN			DOMAIN

1. $x + 4 = 6$ $\{1, ②, 3, 4\}$ **2.** $x + 8 = 11$ $\{1, 2, 3, 5\}$

3. $x + 3 = 3 + x$ $\{1, 2, 3, 4\}$ **4.** $x + 9 = 9 + x$ $\{2, 4, 6, 8\}$

5. $2x + 2 = 4$ $\{1, 2, 3, 4\}$ **6.** $3x + 7 = 19$ $\{1, 2, 3, 4\}$

7. $x + x = 0$ $\{-2, -1, 0, 1, 2\}$ **8.** $x + x = 10$ $\{3, 4, 5, 6\}$

9. $x - x = 0$ $\{-2, -1, 0, 1, 2\}$ **10.** $x - x = 4$ $\{-2, -1, 0, 1, 2\}$

11. $x + 2 = x$ $\{-2, -1, 0, 1, 2\}$ **12.** $x + 5 = x$ $\{-2, -1, 0, 1, 2\}$

13. $3x = 9$ $\{1, 2, 3, 4\}$ **14.** $5x = 15$ $\{1, 2, 3, 4\}$

15. $4x = -12$ $\{-3, -2, -1, 0, 1\}$ **16.** $7x = -14$ $\{-3, -2, -1, 0, 1\}$

17. $4x = 12$ $\{-2, -1, 0, 1, 2\}$ **18.** $7x = 28$ $\{0, 1, 2, 3, 4\}$

19. $2x - 1 = 5$ $\{1, 2, 3, 4\}$ **20.** $5x - 2 = 18$ $\{1, 2, 3, 4\}$

21. $3x = x + 2$ $\{-2, -1, 0, 1, 2\}$ **22.** $5x = x + 12$ $\{1, 2, 3, 4\}$

23. $3x = x + 3$ $\{1, 2, 3, 4\}$ **24.** $5x = x + 10$ $\{1, 2, 3, 4\}$

25. $x(x) = 1$ $\{-2, -1, 0, 1, 2\}$ **26.** $x(x) = 16$ $\{-4, -2, 0, 2, 4\}$

27. $\dfrac{3x}{3} = 3$ $\{1, 2, 3, 4\}$ **28.** $\dfrac{7x}{7} = 7$ $\{1, 2, 3, 4\}$

29. $\dfrac{(x + 1)}{2} = 5$ $\{6, 7, 8, 9\}$ **30.** $\dfrac{(x + 2)}{3} = 3$ $\{6, 7, 8, 9\}$

Checking for Solutions

Name _____

Date _____ Period _____

A domain is given for each equation. Circle all solutions in the domain. If there are no solutions in the domain, cross it out and write ∅.

		DOMAIN			DOMAIN
1. $x + 9 = 10$		$\{1, 2, 3, 4\}$	**2.** $x + 5 = 7$		$\{1, 2, 3, 5\}$
3. $x - 5 = 5 - x$		$\{1, 2, 3, 4\}$	**4.** $x + 2 = 2 + x$		$\{2, 4, 6, 8\}$
5. $2x + 3 = 7$		$\{1, 2, 3, 4\}$	**6.** $5x + 7 = 12$		$\{1, 2, 3, 4\}$
7. $x - x = 0$		$\{-2, -1, 0, 1, 2\}$	**8.** $x - x = 10$		$\{3, 4, 5, 6\}$
9. $x + x = -4$		$\{-2, -1, 0, 1, 2\}$	**10.** $x + x = -2$		$\{-2, -1, 0, 1, 2\}$
11. $x + 2 = 1$		$\{-2, -1, 0, 1, 2\}$	**12.** $x + 4 = 4$		$\{-2, -1, 0, 1, 2\}$
13. $5x = 20$		$\{1, 2, 3, 4\}$	**14.** $4x = 16$		$\{1, 2, 3, 4\}$
15. $2x = -4$		$\{-3, -2, -1, 0, 1\}$	**16.** $9x = -27$		$\{-3, -2, -1, 0, 1\}$
17. $3x = -3$		$\{-2, -1, 0, 1, 2\}$	**18.** $8x = -16$		$\{0, 1, 2, 3, 4\}$
19. $3x - 1 = 11$		$\{1, 2, 3, 4\}$	**20.** $3x - 2 = 4$		$\{1, 2, 3, 4\}$
21. $(2x)2 = x$		$\{-2, -1, 0, 1, 2\}$	**22.** $\dfrac{(7x)}{7} = 2x$		$\{1, 2, 3, 4\}$
23. $\dfrac{12}{(x - 1)} = 4$		$\{1, 2, 3, 4\}$	**24.** $\dfrac{15}{(x + 2)} = 5$		$\{1, 2, 3, 4\}$
25. $\dfrac{16}{x} = 2$		$\{2, 4, 8, 16\}$	**26.** $\dfrac{27}{x} = 3$		$\{3, 6, 9, 12\}$
27. $\dfrac{x}{x} = x$		$\{1, 2, 3, 4\}$	**28.** $\dfrac{x}{x} = 5$		$\{1, 2, 3, 4\}$
29. $\dfrac{(2x + 3)}{5} = 3$		$\{2, 4, 6, 8\}$	**30.** $\dfrac{(3x + 5)}{7} = 2$		$\{3, 6, 9, 12\}$

Developing Skills in Algebra   Book A

Solutions of Equations

Solve.

1. $x + 8 = 12$ _4_

2. $x + 7 = 30$ _____

3. $x - 5 = 20$ _____

4. $x - 13 = 44$ _____

5. $x + 3 = -34$ _____

6. $x + 7 = -22$ _____

7. $x - 14 = -43$ _____

8. $x - 15 = -34$ _____

9. $x + 10 = 100$ _____

10. $x + 14 = 121$ _____

11. $x - 42 = 13$ _____

12. $x - 63 = 17$ _____

13. $x + 91 = 52$ _____

14. $x + 86 = 47$ _____

15. $x + 5 = 13$ _____

16. $x + 9 = 25$ _____

17. $x - 4 = 19$ _____

18. $x - 17 = 22$ _____

19. $x + 5 = -14$ _____

20. $x + 11 = -23$ _____

21. $x - 19 = -14$ _____

22. $x - 23 = -7$ _____

23. $x - 4 = -34$ _____

24. $x - 9 = -27$ _____

25. $x + 27 = -9$ _____

26. $x + 13 = -37$ _____

27. $x + 14 = 3$ _____

28. $x + 22 = 11$ _____

29. $x + 25 = 2$ _____

30. $x + 29 = 4$ _____

31. $x - 14 = -21$ _____

32. $x - 19 = -33$ _____

Solutions of Equations

Name _____

Date _____ Period _____

Solve.

1. $x + 3 = 72$ _69_

2. $x + 4 = 23$ _____

3. $x - 9 = 26$ _____

4. $x - 11 = 31$ _____

5. $x + 8 = -52$ _____

6. $x + 3 = -35$ _____

7. $x - 17 = -37$ _____

8. $x - 21 = -22$ _____

9. $x + 15 = 85$ _____

10. $x + 13 = 97$ _____

11. $x - 55 = 104$ _____

12. $x - 41 = 112$ _____

13. $x + 63 = 46$ _____

14. $x + 91 = 22$ _____

15. $x + 2 = 32$ _____

16. $x + 1 = 28$ _____

17. $x - 6 = 29$ _____

18. $x - 13 = 45$ _____

19. $x + 7 = -22$ _____

20. $x + 13 = -41$ _____

21. $x - 21 = -23$ _____

22. $x - 27 = -11$ _____

23. $x - 7 = -45$ _____

24. $x - 6 = -25$ _____

25. $x + 22 = -15$ _____

26. $x + 19 = -23$ _____

27. $x + 25 = 11$ _____

28. $x + 31 = 22$ _____

29. $x + 36 = 7$ _____

30. $x + 31 = 19$ _____

31. $x - 12 = -36$ _____

32. $x - 29 = -56$ _____

Developing Skills in Algebra   Book A

Solutions of Equations

Name _____

Date _____ Period _____

Solve.

1. $x + \dfrac{1}{4} = 1$ $\dfrac{3}{4}$ **2.** $x + \dfrac{2}{3} = 3$ _____

3. $x - \dfrac{1}{2} = \dfrac{3}{2}$ _____   **4.** $x - \dfrac{4}{5} = \dfrac{2}{5}$ _____

5. $x + \dfrac{7}{8} = 2$ _____   **6.** $x + \dfrac{5}{3} = 3$ _____

7. $x - \dfrac{3}{7} = 5$ _____   **8.** $x - \dfrac{5}{6} = 11$ _____

9. $x + \dfrac{9}{8} = 7$ _____   **10.** $x + \dfrac{17}{11} = 9$ _____

11. $x - \dfrac{5}{8} = \dfrac{3}{4}$ _____   **12.** $x - \dfrac{2}{3} = \dfrac{5}{6}$ _____

13. $x + \dfrac{5}{9} = \dfrac{2}{3}$ _____   **14.** $x + \dfrac{7}{8} = \dfrac{3}{4}$ _____

15. $x - \dfrac{3}{5} = \dfrac{3}{5}$ _____   **16.** $x - \dfrac{2}{3} = \dfrac{5}{3}$ _____

17. $x + 0.25 = 1$ _____   **18.** $x + 0.82 = 4$ _____

19. $x - 0.75 = 9$ _____   **20.** $x + 0.81 = 15$ _____

21. $x + 2.31 = -4.4$ _____   **22.** $x + 5.32 = -3.3$ _____

23. $x - 1.15 = -3.61$ _____   **24.** $x - 3.42 = -5.54$ _____

25. $x + 3.7 = -2.2$ _____   **26.** $x + 4.3 = -8.1$ _____

27. $x - 8.22 = -7$ _____   **28.** $x - 9.94 = -2$ _____

29. $x + 2.2 = 3.5$ _____   **30.** $x + 4.7 = 8.2$ _____

31. $x - 5.3 = 6.21$ _____   **32.** $x - 8.1 = 9.55$ _____

Developing Skills in Algebra   Book A

Solutions of Equations

Name _____

Date _____ Period _____

Solve.

1. $x + \dfrac{1}{3} = 1$ $\dfrac{2}{3}$ **2.** $x + \dfrac{3}{4} = 2$ _____

3. $x - \dfrac{2}{3} = \dfrac{4}{3}$ _____   **4.** $x - \dfrac{5}{8} = \dfrac{3}{8}$ _____

5. $x + \dfrac{3}{5} = 3$ _____   **6.** $x + \dfrac{4}{3} = 2$ _____

7. $x - \dfrac{4}{5} = -5$ _____   **8.** $x - \dfrac{1}{4} = -7$ _____

9. $x + \dfrac{5}{7} = 4$ _____   **10.** $x + \dfrac{8}{9} = 3$ _____

11. $x - \dfrac{2}{3} = \dfrac{1}{6}$ _____   **12.** $x - \dfrac{3}{4} = \dfrac{5}{8}$ _____

13. $x + \dfrac{7}{8} = -\dfrac{3}{4}$ _____   **14.** $x + \dfrac{5}{6} = -\dfrac{2}{3}$ _____

15. $x - \dfrac{4}{7} = \dfrac{4}{7}$ _____   **16.** $x - \dfrac{3}{5} = \dfrac{3}{5}$ _____

17. $x + 1.35 = 2$ _____   **18.** $x + 2.31 = 3$ _____

19. $x - 4.75 = -3$ _____   **20.** $x + 2.34 = -7$ _____

21. $x + 1.35 = -2.3$ _____   **22.** $x + 2.22 = -4.1$ _____

23. $x - 2.34 = -5.52$ _____   **24.** $x - 5.77 = -7.33$ _____

25. $x + 6.1 = -5.3$ _____   **26.** $x + 2.7 = -6.8$ _____

27. $x - 4.31 = -8$ _____   **28.** $x - 3.51 = -9$ _____

29. $x + 5.4 = 2.1$ _____   **30.** $x + 6.3 = 5.7$ _____

31. $x - 4.9 = 4.62$ _____   **32.** $x - 3.6 = 4.32$ _____

Developing Skills in Algebra   Book A

Solutions of Equations

Name _____

Date _____ Period _____

Solve.

1. $5x = 10$ _2_

2. $2x = 4$ _____

3. $3x = -6$ _____

4. $4x = -12$ _____

5. $13x = 91$ _____

6. $21x = 147$ _____

7. $-6y = 84$ _____

8. $-8y = 96$ _____

9. $9z = -9$ _____

10. $12z = -36$ _____

11. $-4u = 0$ _____

12. $10u = 0$ _____

13. $-16p = -128$ _____

14. $-23p = -161$ _____

15. $-x = 115$ _____

16. $-x = 108$ _____

17. $36x = 18$ _____

18. $15x = 45$ _____

19. $85x = -17$ _____

20. $48x = -12$ _____

21. $98x = 14$ _____

22. $102x = 17$ _____

23. $-x = 4$ _____

24. $-x = 20$ _____

25. $36x = 27$ _____

26. $45x = 60$ _____

27. $-15x = 6$ _____

28. $-28x = 21$ _____

29. $14x = -35$ _____

30. $24x = -36$ _____

31. $12x = 32$ _____

32. $16x = 20$ _____

Solutions of Equations

Name _____

Date _____ Period _____

Solve.

1. $3x = 9$ _3_

2. $4x = 16$ _____

3. $5x = -20$ _____

4. $2x = -14$ _____

5. $15x = 90$ _____

6. $17x = 102$ _____

7. $-7y = 84$ _____

8. $-9y = 108$ _____

9. $13z = 91$ _____

10. $18z = -162$ _____

11. $-7u = -14$ _____

12. $-9u = -27$ _____

13. $-24p = 0$ _____

14. $-14p = 0$ _____

15. $-x = -14$ _____

16. $-x = -99$ _____

17. $42x = 7$ _____

18. $27x = 9$ _____

19. $72x = -12$ _____

20. $56x = -14$ _____

21. $90x = 45$ _____

22. $133x = 19$ _____

23. $-x = 7$ _____

24. $-x = 14$ _____

25. $45x = 24$ _____

26. $24x = 15$ _____

27. $-30x = 12$ _____

28. $-44x = 22$ _____

29. $28x = -42$ _____

30. $15x = -42$ _____

31. $18x = 24$ _____

32. $20x = 15$ _____

64

Solutions of Equations

Name _____

Date _____ Period _____

Solve.

1. $\frac{1}{2}x = 5$ _10_   **2.** $\frac{1}{3}x = 2$ _____

3. $\frac{1}{4}x = 3$ _____   **4.** $\frac{1}{5}x = 1$ _____

5. $\frac{1}{7}x = -3$ _____   **6.** $\frac{1}{6}x = -2$ _____

7. $\frac{1}{8}x = -1$ _____   **8.** $\frac{1}{9}x = -3$ _____

9. $\frac{-1}{2}x = 4$ _____   **10.** $\frac{-1}{5}x = 2$ _____

11. $\frac{-1}{4}x = 7$ _____   **12.** $\frac{-1}{3}x = 9$ _____

13. $\frac{-1}{7}x = -2$ _____   **14.** $\frac{-1}{9}x = -7$ _____

15. $\frac{2}{5}x = 12$ _____   **16.** $\frac{3}{4}x = 9$ _____

17. $\frac{3}{8}z = 12$ _____   **18.** $\frac{4}{5}z = 16$ _____

19. $\frac{5}{6}k = 30$ _____   **20.** $\frac{7}{8}k = 21$ _____

21. $\frac{-1}{3}a = 18$ _____   **22.** $\frac{5}{7}b = -50$ _____

23. $\frac{-4}{9}c = -20$ _____   **24.** $\frac{-6}{7}d = 36$ _____

25. $\frac{3}{5}e = -24$ _____   **26.** $\frac{4}{7}f = -32$ _____

27. $\frac{x}{5} = 32$ _____   **28.** $\frac{y}{7} = 15$ _____

29. $\frac{2x}{9} = 22$ _____   **30.** $\frac{3y}{7} = 24$ _____

31. $\frac{-4a}{13} = 44$ _____   **32.** $\frac{-5x}{11} = 35$ _____

Solutions of Equations

Solve.

1. $\frac{1}{2}x = 4$ _____8_____   **2.** $\frac{1}{5}x = 3$ _____

3. $\frac{1}{3}x = 6$ _____   **4.** $\frac{1}{5}x = 2$ _____

5. $\frac{1}{7}x = -1$ _____   **6.** $\frac{1}{6}x = -4$ _____

7. $\frac{1}{9}x = -2$ _____   **8.** $\frac{1}{5}x = -7$ _____

9. $\frac{-1}{3}x = 2$ _____   **10.** $\frac{-1}{8}x = 7$ _____

11. $\frac{-1}{2}x = 15$ _____   **12.** $\frac{-1}{5}x = 0$ _____

13. $\frac{-1}{4}x = -7$ _____   **14.** $\frac{-1}{7}x = -2$ _____

15. $\frac{2}{3}x = 0$ _____   **16.** $\frac{5}{8}x = 10$ _____

17. $\frac{3}{5}z = 18$ _____   **18.** $\frac{2}{9}z = 20$ _____

19. $\frac{4}{5}k = 28$ _____   **20.** $\frac{5}{7}k = 35$ _____

21. $\frac{-1}{4}a = 12$ _____   **22.** $\frac{3}{5}b = -45$ _____

23. $\frac{-2}{7}c = -6$ _____   **24.** $\frac{-4}{5}d = 20$ _____

25. $\frac{4}{5}e = -24$ _____   **26.** $\frac{3}{7}f = -33$ _____

27. $\frac{x}{2} = 15$ _____   **28.** $\frac{y}{3} = 12$ _____

29. $\frac{3x}{7} = 21$ _____   **30.** $\frac{4y}{9} = 32$ _____

31. $\frac{-4a}{15} = 44$ _____   **32.** $\frac{-3x}{11} = 39$ _____

Solutions of Equations

Name _____

Date _____ Period _____

Solve.

1. $2x - 5 = 11$ _8_

2. $3x - 4 = 14$ _____

3. $5x - 7 = 13$ _____

4. $2x - 11 = 7$ _____

5. $4x + 1 = 9$ _____

6. $7x - 2 = 12$ _____

7. $8x + 3 = 19$ _____

8. $10x + 7 = 27$ _____

9. $-3x - 4 = 8$ _____

10. $-5x - 8 = 12$ _____

11. $-6x + 3 = -9$ _____

12. $-4x + 5 = -15$ _____

13. $2x + 25 = 13$ _____

14. $7x + 32 = 4$ _____

15. $14 - x = 22$ _____

16. $73 - x = 18$ _____

17. $2x + 7 = 13$ _____

18. $5x - 3 = 12$ _____

19. $-4x + 10 = 38$ _____

20. $-5x + 8 = 48$ _____

21. $-12x - 17 = -89$ _____

22. $-15x - 28 = -73$ _____

23. $6x + 14 = -64$ _____

24. $9x + 13 = -68$ _____

25. $13x - 29 = 153$ _____

26. $17x - 35 = 271$ _____

27. $7x + 15 = -20$ _____

28. $9x + 19 = -35$ _____

29. $16x - 55 = 41$ _____

30. $19x - 32 = 63$ _____

31. $45 - 13x = 58$ _____

32. $28 - 32x = 92$ _____

    Developing Skills in Algebra   Book A

Solutions of Equations   Name _____

                                          Date _____ Period _____

_____

Solve.

1. $3x - 4 = 11$ _____5_____   **2.** $5x - 3 = 12$ _____

3. $4x - 9 = 15$ _____   **4.** $2x - 19 = 3$ _____

5. $5x + 3 = 28$ _____   **6.** $6x + 5 = 35$ _____

7. $3x + 1 = 34$ _____   **8.** $12x + 5 = 41$ _____

9. $-2x - 5 = 7$ _____   **10.** $-4x - 7 = 25$ _____

11. $-3x - 7 = -28$ _____   **12.** $-5x + 7 = -38$ _____

13. $2x + 33 = 17$ _____   **14.** $6x + 25 = 1$ _____

15. $17 - x = 4$ _____   **16.** $29 - x = 8$ _____

17. $3x + 5 = 26$ _____   **18.** $4x - 7 = 33$ _____

19. $-5x + 11 = 41$ _____   **20.** $-7x + 3 = 45$ _____

21. $-11x - 20 = -97$ _____   **22.** $-13x - 14 = -131$ _____

23. $8x + 11 = -37$ _____   **24.** $7x - 13 = -76$ _____

25. $12x - 32 = 112$ _____   **26.** $14x - 22 = 160$ _____

27. $5x + 17 = -38$ _____   **28.** $8x + 27 = -109$ _____

29. $14x - 32 = 234$ _____   **30.** $23x - 45 = 116$ _____

31. $31 - 12x = 211$ -_____   **32.** $43 - 21x = 232$ _____

Solutions of Equations

Name _____

Date _____ Period _____

Solve.

1. $\frac{x}{3} + 10 = 15$ ___*15*___

2. $\frac{x}{2} - 7 = 9$ _____

3. $\frac{x}{7} - 4 = 2$ _____

4. $\frac{x}{5} - 3 = 6$ _____

5. $\frac{x}{2} + 13 = 5$ _____

6. $\frac{x}{4} + 18 = 5$ _____

7. $\frac{x}{11} + 21 = 7$ _____

8. $\frac{x}{10} + 32 = 11$ _____

9. $\frac{x}{5} - 16 = -3$ _____

10. $\frac{x}{3} - 15 = -7$ _____

11. $\frac{1}{4}x + 5 = 15$ _____

12. $\frac{1}{6}x + 9 = 12$ _____

13. $4 - \frac{1}{7}x = 13$ _____

14. $8 - \frac{1}{5}x = 5$ _____

15. $\frac{1}{2}x + 13 = 9$ _____

16. $\frac{1}{3}x + 16 = 11$ _____

17. $\frac{1}{4}x - 15 = -7$ _____

18. $\frac{1}{8}x - 17 = -8$ _____

19. $\frac{2x}{3} + 15 = 17$ _____

20. $\frac{3x}{4} + 17 = 23$ _____

21. $11 - \frac{4x}{5} = 19$ _____

22. $13 - \frac{3x}{2} = 37$ _____

23. $\frac{2x}{5} + 17 = 9$ _____

24. $\frac{5x}{7} + 28 = 8$ _____

25. $\frac{3}{4}x - 7 = 14$ _____

26. $\frac{2}{3}x - 9 = 11$ _____

27. $\frac{3}{4}x - 9 = 27$ _____

28. $\frac{5}{7}x - 13 = 82$ _____

29. $28 - \frac{2}{3}x = 46$ _____

30. $67 - \frac{3}{4}x = 85$ _____

31. $53 - \frac{5}{8}x = -102$ _____

32. $81 - \frac{4}{7}x = 21$ _____

Developing Skills in Algebra   Book A

Solutions of Equations

Name _____

Date _____ Period _____

Solve.

1. $\dfrac{x}{2} + 13 = 17$ _____8_____

2. $\dfrac{x}{4} - 3 = 15$ _____

3. $\dfrac{x}{5} - 9 = 7$ _____

4. $\dfrac{x}{3} - 8 = 13$ _____

5. $\dfrac{x}{7} + 11 = 1$ _____

6. $\dfrac{x}{4} + 13 = 6$ _____

7. $\dfrac{x}{13} + 11 = 9$ _____

8. $\dfrac{x}{15} + 23 = 27$ _____

9. $\dfrac{x}{5} - 18 = -11$ _____

10. $\dfrac{x}{2} - 13 = -9$ _____

11. $\dfrac{1}{4}x + 9 = 13$ _____

12. $\dfrac{1}{6}x + 8 = 15$ _____

13. $8 - \dfrac{1}{3}x = 16$ _____

14. $5 - \dfrac{1}{4}x = 11$ _____

15. $\dfrac{1}{5}x + 27 = 22$ _____

16. $\dfrac{1}{7}x + 19 = 21$ _____

17. $\dfrac{1}{2}x - 29 = -22$ _____

18. $\dfrac{1}{3}x - 26 = -25$ _____

19. $\dfrac{3x}{5} + 22 = 28$ _____

20. $\dfrac{5x}{8} + 13 = 18$ _____

21. $14 - \dfrac{2x}{3} = 18$ _____

22. $19 - \dfrac{5x}{2} = 34$ _____

23. $\dfrac{3x}{5} + 22 = 16$ _____

24. $\dfrac{4x}{3} + 25 = 33$ _____

25. $\dfrac{2}{3}x - 3 = 11$ _____

26. $\dfrac{5}{7}x - 4 = 21$ _____

27. $\dfrac{4}{9}x + 7 = 31$ _____

28. $\dfrac{3}{8}x - 14 = 1$ _____

29. $17 - \dfrac{5}{9}x = 27$ _____

30. $53 - \dfrac{2}{3}x = 59$ _____

31. $41 - \dfrac{3}{8}x = -22$ _____

32. $28 - \dfrac{2}{5}x = 34$ _____

Developing Skills in Algebra   Book A

Solutions of Equations

Name _____

Date _____ Period _____

_____

Solve.

1. $16x + 42 - 13x = 24$ *-6*

2. $17x - 19 - 8x = 53$ _____

3. $23x - 14 - 7x = 82$ _____

4. $53x - 18 + 7x = 162$ _____

5. $14x + 43 - 25x = 219$ _____

6. $18x + 51 - 47x = 225$ _____

7. $-17x - 22 - 8x = 128$ _____

8. $-25x - 17 - 18x = 284$ _____

9. $28x + 39 + 7x = 319$ _____

10. $34x + 36 + 9x = 337$ _____

11. $13x + 12 - 19x = -24$ _____

12. $25x + 13 - 33x = -11$ _____

13. $19x - 22 + 7x = 30$ _____

14. $35x + 58 + 12x = -130$ _____

15. $14x + 25 - 11x = 37$ _____

16. $23x + 18 - 12x = 62$ _____

17. $37x - 14 + 19x = 154$ _____

18. $31x - 22 + 11x = 188$ _____

19. $36x - 21 - 24x = -105$ _____

20. $41x - 33 - 25x = -145$ _____

21. $51x + 18 - 29x = -114$ _____

22. $57x + 23 - 42x = -97$ _____

23. $48x - 13 - 24x = 131$ _____

24. $33x - 21 - 9x = 171$ _____

25. $55x + 21 + 17x = 165$ _____

26. $29x + 33 + 14x = 162$ _____

27. $23x + 18 + 24x = -358$ _____

28. $14x + 17 + 19x = -115$ _____

29. $52x - 14 - 35x = -133$ _____

30. $45x - 21 - 19x = -255$ _____

31. $66x - 37 - 23x = 49$ _____

32. $43x - 22 - 18x = 28$ _____

© 1984 by Dale Seymour Publications   71   Developing Skills in Algebra   Book A

Solutions of Equations

All algebra steps must be shown neatly on notebook paper or zero.

Name _____

Date _____ Period _____

Solve.

1. $12x + 23 - 7x = 68$ _9_

2. $19x + 39 - 4x = 9$ _____

3. $19x + 59 + 8x = 5$ _____

4. $45x - 83 + 9x = 25$ _____

5. $21x + 75 - 29x = 19$ _____

6. $43x + 51 - 57x = 23$ _____

7. $-22x - 25 - 9x = 99$ _____

8. $-14x - 23 - 15x = 151$ _____

9. $17x - 23 + 9x = 237$ _____

10. $24x + 81 + 7x = 19$ _____

11. $45x + 21 - 17x = -63$ _____

12. $27x + 19 - 39x = -65$ _____

13. $23x - 45 - 38x = -15$ _____

14. $48x - 13 - 51x = -64$ _____

15. $35x + 13 - 18x = 166$ _____

16. $45x + 22 - 22x = 229$ _____

17. $17x - 32 + 24x = 132$ _____

18. $13x - 41 + 17x = 229$ _____

19. $48x - 29 - 13x = -134$ _____

20. $59x - 21 - 44x = -51$ _____

21. $23x + 37 - 45x = -139$ _____

22. $15x + 54 - 39x = -90$ _____

23. $75x - 29 - 53x = 59$ _____

24. $47x - 43 - 8x = 308$ _____

25. $16x + 43 - 39x = 89$ _____

26. $13x + 57 - 44x = 274$ _____

27. $25x + 125 + 13x = 11$ _____

28. $19x + 214 + 6x = 39$ _____

29. $46x - 63 - 25x = -147$ _____

30. $63x - 44 - 47x = -140$ _____

31. $23x - 89 - 42x = 63$ _____

32. $14x - 53 - 32x = 73$ _____

Developing Skills in Algebra   Book A

Name _____

Date _____ Period _____

Solve.

1. $4(2x + 7) = 108$ _____10_____

2. $5(3x + 8) = 175$ _____

3. $8(3x + 1) = 128$ _____

4. $-4(2x + 11) = 92$ _____

5. $-6(5x + 2) = 198$ _____

6. $-7(3x - 1) = 91$ _____

7. $8(3x - 1) = -80$ _____

8. $5(9x - 4) = 25$ _____

9. $-7(4x - 7) = 105$ _____

10. $4(3x - 9) = 96$ _____

11. $3(4x - 7) = 135$ _____

12. $8(2x - 4) = 96$ _____

13. $10(5x - 3) = 20$ _____

14. $9(7x - 4) = 27$ _____

15. $7(2x - 4) = 28$ _____

16. $9(5x - 2) = 117$ _____

17. $4(7x + 6) = 80$ _____

18. $6(3x + 11) = 30$ _____

19. $4x - 5(3x + 10) = 126$ _____

20. $5x - 4(2x + 11) = 13$ _____

21. $7x - 2(3 + 4x) = 19$ _____

22. $17x - 3(4 + 5x) = 44$ _____

23. $15 + 3(2x - 9) = 60$ _____

24. $10x - 3(8 - 5x) = -74$ _____

25. $28 - 6(2x + 4) = 124$ _____

26. $35 - 5(2x + 3) = 20$ _____

27. $3(2x - 1) + 5 = 14$ _____

28. $8(3x - 5) + 20 = -68$ _____

29. $3(7x + 9) = -15$ _____

30. $4(3x + 2) - 18 = 14$ _____

31. $15 - (2x + 7) = 14$ _____

32. $17 - (6x + 3) = -16$ _____

Developing Skills in Algebra   Book A

Solutions of Equations

Name _____

Date _____ Period _____

Solve.

1. $3(3x + 5) = 96$ ___9___

2. $2(5x + 7) = 34$ _____

3. $5(4x + 3) = 75$ _____

4. $-6(3x - 8) = -6$ _____

5. $-4(7x + 5) = -160$ _____

6. $-3(8x - 4) = 180$ _____

7. $-7(2x - 5) = 161$ _____

8. $9(3x - 8) = 36$ _____

9. $6(5x + 12) = 162$ _____

10. $2(7x + 15) = 128$ _____

11. $5(6x - 9) = -15$ _____

12. $4(9x - 14) = 16$ _____

13. $14(3x - 5) = 56$ _____

14. $11(4x - 9) = -319$ _____

15. $5(7x - 8) = -320$ _____

16. $8(3x - 9) = 0$ _____

17. $-6(7x + 5) = 12$ _____

18. $-8(3x + 7) = 16$ _____

19. $3x + 2(5x - 3) = 7$ _____

20. $7x + 3(4x - 1) = -79$ _____

21. $3x + 4(3x - 5) = 25$ _____

22. $7x + 9(2x - 4) = 14$ _____

23. $8x + 3(2 - 3x) = 28$ _____

24. $14x + 5(4 - 2x) = 20$ _____

25. $18 + 4(3x - 7) = -70$ _____

26. $13 + 8(5x - 9) = 21$ _____

27. $15 - 5(4x - 7) = 50$ _____

28. $18 - 6(5x - 8) = -24$ _____

29. $-4(5x - 2) + 7 = -5$ _____

30. $-6(2x - 3) + 15 = 9$ _____

31. $-(6x + 7) + 8 = 19$ _____

32. $-(5x + 8) + 12 = 34$ _____

Name _____

Date _____ Period _____

Solve.

1. $2x = 5x - 3$ _____/_____   **2.** $4x = 7x - 12$ _____

3. $3y = y - 6$ _____   **4.** $7y = y - 12$ _____

5. $6x = 3x + 12$ _____   **6.** $9z = 5z + 16$ _____

7. $108 + 4u = -2u$ _____   **8.** $15p + p = 7 - 12p$ _____

9. $12d + 4 = 8d$ _____   **10.** $9m - 22 = 4m + 3$ _____

11. $5u - u = u + 15$ _____   **12.** $8u - u = u + 24$ _____

13. $12p + p = 5 - 2p$ _____   **14.** $18p + p = 11 - 3p$ _____

15. $5m - 18 = 6m + 4$ _____   **16.** $11m - 23 = 12m + 5$ _____

17. $26n + 15 = 32n + 3$ _____   **18.** $35n + 12 = 40n + 42$ _____

19. $16b - 4 = 38b + 84$ _____   **20.** $14b - 2 = 19b + 33$ _____

21. $5(z + 6) = 8z$ _____   **22.** $3(z + 8) = 7z$ _____

23. $7(7 - 3u) = -u - 11$ _____   **24.** $4(8 - 5u) = -2u - 4$ _____

25. $8(4 - u) + u = 8 + u$ _____   **26.** $6(7 - u) + u = 36 + u$ _____

27. $3(u - 3) = 4(u + 3)$ _____   **28.** $7(u - 8) = 3(u + 4)$ _____

29. $-3(x + 5) = 2(x + 5)$ _____   **30.** $-5(x + 2) = 3(x + 2)$ _____

31. $-4(3x + 2) = 3(6x - 6)$ _____   **32.** $-7(4x + 2) = 5(2x + 1)$ _____

75   Developing Skills in Algebra   Book A

Solutions of Equations Name _____

Date _____ Period _____

Solve.

1. $3x = 4x - 7$ _7_

2. $5x = 9x - 16$ _____

3. $7y = 2y - 15$ _____

4. $4y = y - 21$ _____

5. $9x = 2x + 14$ _____

6. $8z = 3z + 30$ _____

7. $99 + 6u = -3u$ _____

8. $13p + 2p = 29 - 14p$ _____

9. $13d + 25 = 8d$ _____

10. $6m - 14 = 2m + 6$ _____

11. $7u - 2u = 3u + 22$ _____

12. $9u - 3u = 2u + 24$ _____

13. $17p + p = 40 - 2p$ _____

14. $44 + 7p = -4p$ _____

15. $2m - 21 = 9m + 7$ _____

16. $15m - 25 = 9m + 17$ _____

17. $18n + 12 = 27n + 3$ _____

18. $41n + 18 = 49n + 42$ _____

19. $15b - 8 = 31b + 24$ _____

20. $19b - 10 = 35b + 22$ _____

21. $3(z + 5) = 8z$ _____

22. $2(z + 7) = 9z$ _____

23. $5(4 - 7u) = -u - 48$ _____

24. $6(5 - 3u) = -4u - 12$ _____

25. $7(3 - u) + u = 5 - 2u$ _____

26. $4(3 - u) + u = 22 + 2u$ _____

27. $5(1 + c) = 6(2 + c)$ _____

28. $9(3 + c) = 4(3 + c)$ _____

29. $5(x + 7) = 6(x - 5)$ _____

30. $9(x - 4) = 3(x + 12)$ _____

31. $6(2x - 1) = -5(3x - 15)$ _____

32. $8(3x + 1) = 7(2x + 4)$ _____

Developing Skills in Algebra   Book A

Writing and Solving Equations

Name _____

Date _____ Period _____

For each figure, write an equation using the perimeter. Then solve for z.

1. equation: _17 = z + 2 + 6 + 4_

z = _5_

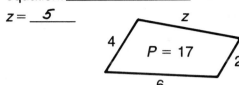

2. equation: _____

z _____

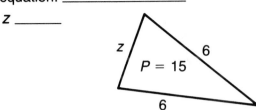

3. equation: _____

z = _____

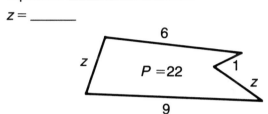

4. equation: _____

z = _____

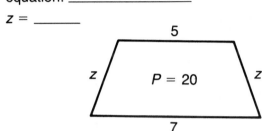

5. equation: _____

z = _____

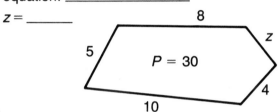

6. equation: _____

z = _____

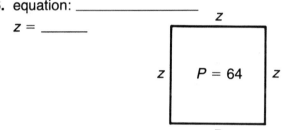

7. equation: _____

z = _____

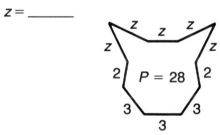

8. equation: _____

z = _____

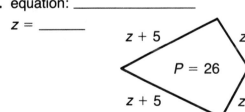

9. equation: _____

z = _____

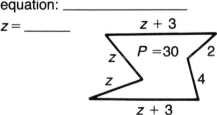

10. equation: _____

z = _____

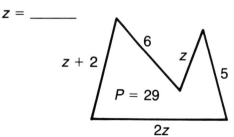

11. equation: _____

z = _____

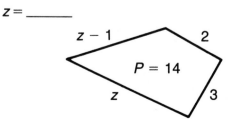

12. equation: _____

z = _____

Developing Skills in Algebra   Book A

Writing and Solving Equations

Name _____

Date _____ Period _____

In the figures below, all angles are right angles.
Write an equation for each variable and solve it. Then find the perimeter of each figure.

1. $x =$ ___3___
  $y =$ ___2___
  $P =$ ___18___

$x = 5 - 2$
$y + 2 = 4$
$P = 2 + y + x + 2 + 5 + 4$

2. $x =$ _____
  $y =$ _____
  $P =$ _____

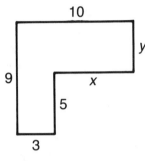

3. $x =$ _____
  $y =$ _____
  $P =$ _____

4. $x =$ _____
  $y =$ _____
  $P =$ _____

5. $x =$ _____
  $y =$ _____
  $P =$ _____

6. $x =$ _____
  $y =$ _____
  $P =$ _____

7. $x =$ _____
  $y =$ _____
  $P =$ _____

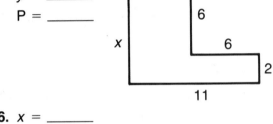

8. $x =$ _____
  $y =$ _____
  $P =$ _____

9. $x =$ _____
  $y =$ _____
  $P =$ _____

10. $x =$ _____
  $y =$ _____
  $P =$ _____

Developing Skills in Algebra Book A

Equations Having More Than One Variable

Name _____

Date _____ Period _____

Solve for the variable specified. Assume domains include only values that give nonzero denominators.

1. $a + b = c$ for b $b = c - a$

2. $x + y = z$ for y _____

3. $2m + y = r$ for y _____

4. $3t + u = v$ for u _____

5. $a - b = c$ for a _____

6. $x - y = z$ for x _____

7. $a - b = c$ for b _____

8. $x - y = z$ for y _____

9. $2t + u = v$ for t _____

10. $2x + y = z$ for x _____

11. $\frac{1}{2}x + y = 10$ for x _____

12. $\frac{1}{3}a + b = 7$ for a _____

13. $ab = c$ for a _____

14. $xy = z$ for x _____

15. $3 + ab = c$ for a _____

16. $-4 + xy = z$ for x _____

17. $x - 2y = z$ for y _____

18. $a - 2b = c$ for b _____

19. $3a + 2b = c$ for a _____

20. $4m + 3n = p$ for m _____

21. $3a + 2b = c$ for b _____

22. $4m + 3n = p$ for n _____

23. $5a - 3b = c$ for a _____

24. $6m - 4n = p$ for m _____

25. $2 - ab = c$ for a _____

26. $4 - xy = z$ for x _____

27. $mnp = q$ for n _____

28. $abc = d$ for b _____

29. $\frac{x}{y} + 2 = z$ for x _____

30. $\frac{a}{b} + 3 = c$ for a _____

31. $2 + \frac{x}{y} - z = m$ for x _____

32. $-3 + \frac{a}{b} + c = t$ for a _____

Equations Having More Than One Variable   Name _____

Date _____ Period _____

Solve for the variable specified. Assume domains include only values that give nonzero denominators.

1. $m + 2n = p$ for m $m = \underline{p} - 2n$ **2.** $2m + n = p$ for m _____

3. $a - 2b = c$ for a _____   **4.** $2a - b = c$ for a _____

5. $a + 2b = c$ for b _____   **6.** $a + 2b = c$ for a _____

7. $c - d = b$ for c _____   **8.** $c - d = z$ for d _____

9. $3x - y = z$ for x _____   **10.** $5x - 2y = 3z$ for x _____

11. $\frac{1}{3}x + 2y = 5$ for x _____   **12.** $\frac{1}{4}x + 3y = 4$ for x _____

13. $mn = r$ for m _____   **14.** $mn = r$ for n _____

15. $5 + xy = z$ for x _____   **16.** $-4 + ab = c$ for a _____

17. $a - 3b = 2c$ for b _____   **18.** $r - 5s = t$ for s _____

19. $4x + 3y = 7$ for x _____   **20.** $4x + 3y = 7$ for y _____

21. $2s - 3t = 4$ for t _____   **22.** $2s - 3t = 4$ for s _____

23. $4m - 7n = p$ for m _____   **24.** $8a - 3b = c$ for a _____

25. $5a - 3b = c$ for b _____   **26.** $6m - 4n = p$ for n _____

27. $ab + 2 = c$ for a _____   **28.** $xy + 4 = z$ for x _____

29. $\frac{x}{y} = z$ for x _____   **30.** $\frac{a}{b} = c$ for a _____

31. $4 - \frac{m}{n} = p$ for m _____   **32.** $8 - \frac{r}{s} = t$ for r _____

Equations Having More Than One Variable   Name _____

                                               Date _____ Period _____

Solve for *y*.

1. $2x + y = 7$ $y = \underline{7 - 2x}$ **2.** $4x + y = 9$ _____

3. $-x + 4y = 9$ _____   **4.** $7x + 2y = 5$ _____

5. $3x - y = 12$ _____   **6.** $6x + 5y = 12$ _____

7. $-2x - 3y = 10$ _____   **8.** $-x + 6y = 3$ _____

9. $x + \frac{1}{2}y = 6$ _____   **10.** $x + \frac{1}{4}y = 10$ _____

11. $3x + \frac{2}{3}y = 15$ _____   **12.** $7x - y = 13$ _____

13. $x + \frac{y}{5} = 10$ _____   **14.** $7x + \frac{5y}{6} = 6$ _____

15. $2x + \frac{3y}{7} = 9$ _____   **16.** $4x + \frac{3}{4}y = 11$ _____

Solve for the variable specified. Assume domains include only values that give nonzero denominators.

17. $d = rt$ for *t* $t = \underline{\frac{d}{r}}$ **18.** $d = rt$ for *r*   _____

19. $A = bh$ for *h*   _____   **20.** $A = bh$ for *b*   _____

21. $p = 2(L + W)$ for *L*   _____   **22.** $A = \frac{1}{2}bh$ for *h*   _____

23. $C = 2\pi r$ for *r*   _____   **24.** $V = \pi r^2 h$ for *h*   _____

25. $A = \frac{h}{2}(a + b)$ for *a*   _____   **26.** $A = \frac{h}{2}(a + b)$ for *b*   _____

27. $i = prt$ for *r*   _____   **28.** $E = IR$ for *R*   _____

29. $S = \frac{n}{2}(a + 1)$ for *n*   _____   **30.** $L = a + d(n - 1)$ for *a*   _____

                   Developing Skills in Algebra   Book A

Equations Having More Than One Variable

Solve for y.

1. $3x + y = 5$ $y = \underline{5 - 3x}$ 2. $2x + y = 7$ _____

3. $8x + 4y = 12$ _____   4. $4x + 2y = 8$ _____

5. $5x - y = 13$ _____   6. $8x - y = 13$ _____

7. $-3x - 4y = 13$ _____   8. $-5x + 3y = 7$ _____

9. $2x + \frac{1}{3}y = 7$ _____   10. $5x + \frac{1}{2}y = 4$ _____

11. $7x - \frac{3}{4}y = 5$ _____   12. $6x - \frac{2}{3}y = 9$ _____

13. $x + \frac{y}{3} = 12$ _____   14. $x + \frac{y}{7} = 10$ _____

15. $5x + \frac{2y}{3} = 4$ _____   16. $7x + \frac{5y}{2} = 9$ _____

Solve for the variable specified. Assume domains include only values that give nonzero denominators.

17. $p = a + b + c$ for c $c = \underline{p - a - b}$ 18. $V = LWH$ for H _____

19. $A = h(b_1 + b_2)$ for h _____   20. $V = \frac{1}{2}abh$ for b _____

21. $V = \frac{1}{3}Bh$ for B _____   22. $V = \frac{4}{3}\pi r^3$ for π _____

23. $p = 4s$ for s _____   24. $A = \frac{1}{2}d_1 d_2$ for d_1 _____

25. $S = 180(n - 2)$ for n _____   26. $A = p(1 + rt)$ for r _____

27. $L = a + d(n - 1)$ for d _____   28. $S = \frac{n}{2}(a + 1)$ for a _____

29. $F = \frac{WH}{L}$ for H _____   30. $K = \frac{lEh}{1000}$ for h _____

Name _____

Date _____ Period _____

Translate each expression into an algebraic expression.

1. Eighteen more than *x*   _*x* + 18_____

2. Five less than *y*   _____

3. The sum of seven and *x*   _____

4. Ten subtracted from *y*   _____

5. The difference between 7 and *x* _____

6. The product of five and *x*   _____

7. The quotient of seven and *y*   _____

8. The number *h* decreased by 2   _____

9. The number *m* increased by 7   _____

10. Fifteen increased by *x*   _____

11. Twenty decreased by *y*   _____

12. Twelve multiplied by *x*   _____

13. Twenty-three divided by *n*   _____

14. The number *x* multiplied by five _____

15. The sum of *m* and *n*   _____

16. The difference between *r* and *s* _____

Translating Word Expressions

Name _____

Date _____ Period _____

Translate each expression into an algebraic expression.

1. Twenty-five more than r $25 + r$

2. Twelve less than z _____

3. The sum of nine and m _____

4. Eleven subtracted from y _____

5. The difference between x and two   _____

6. The product of m and four   _____

7. The quotient of y and ten   _____

8. The number three decreased by x _____

9. The number nine increased by eight   _____

10. The number x increased by twenty   _____

11. The number z increased by twelve   _____

12. Fifteen multiplied by c _____

13. Forty-six divided by x _____

14. The number six multiplied by x _____

15. The sum of r and s _____

16. The difference between p and q _____

      Developing Skills in Algebra   Book A

Name _____

Date _____ Period _____

Translate each expression into an algebraic expression, using parentheses as necessary.

1. The number z multiplied by the sum of x and y $z(x+y)$

2. The sum of k and 7 divided by v _____

3. The number m divided by the sum of z and u _____

4. The product of a, b, and c decreased by d _____

5. The number p subtracted from the product of 10 and x _____

6. Two times the difference between n and 4   _____

7. The number r added to the product of a and c _____

8. Five multiplied by the difference between b and k _____

9. The product of fourteen and c, decreased by d _____

10. The sum of r and 9, divided by k _____

11. Seven times the difference between d and eleven   _____

12. The number a multiplied by the sum of b and c _____

13. The number u subtracted from the product of r and s _____

14. The number s divided by the sum of t and u _____

15. The sum of r and s, multiplied by five   _____

16. The difference between r and s, multiplied by t _____

Translating Word Expressions   Name _____

                                                Date _____ Period _____

Translate each expression into an algebraic expression, using parentheses as necessary.

1. The product of nine and *r*, decreased by *t* $9r - t$

2. The sum of *m* and ten multiplied by 4   _____

3. The sum of *a* and *b*, divided by *c*   _____

4. The number *x* subtracted from the product of *y* and *z*   _____

5. The product of four times the difference of *a* and *b*   _____

6. The sum of five and *x*, divided by *y*   _____

7. The number *c* subtracted from the product of *r* and *s*   _____

8. Three times the difference of *p* and *q*   _____

9. The number *a* times the difference between *b* and *c*   _____

10. The product of *z* and the difference between 7 and *a*   _____

11. Six more than the product of *r* and *t*   _____

12. The number seven, divided by the sum of *p* and *q*   _____

13. Three times the difference between 5*x* and *y*   _____

14. The number five divided by the sum of *c* and *d*   _____

15. The product of *m* and *n* increased by eight   _____

16. The number *a* multiplied by the sum of 7 and *x*   _____

Translating Algebraic Expressions   Name _____

                                           Date _____ Period _____

Translate each expression into a word expression.

1. $a(b + c)$ *the number a multiplied by the sum of b and c*

2. $rs - 8$ _____

3. $x(y - z)$ _____

4. $rs + tu$ _____

5. $mn - 4$ _____

6. $J(w + v)$ _____

7. $\dfrac{u}{p} + 6$ _____

8. $(t - 17)11$ _____

9. $d - xy$ _____

10. $(a + b) - ru$ _____

11. $xy + ab$ _____

12. $\dfrac{r + t}{r - t}$ _____

13. $abc - 3$ _____

14. $\dfrac{m}{n} - 25$ _____

15. $J - (t - b)$ _____

16. $(k - 5)u$ _____

Name _____

Date _____ Period _____

Translate each expression into a word expression.

1. $m - rs$ *the difference between m and the product of r and s*

2. $a(b + c)$ _____

3. $vw + xy$ _____

4. $a(c + d)$ _____

5. $r(s - t)$ _____

6. $(v - 5)11$ _____

7. $x - (y - z)$ _____

8. $\dfrac{pq}{rt}$ _____

9. $(a - b)(a + b)$ _____

10. $rst - 27$ _____

11. $\dfrac{x + y}{x - y}$ _____

12. $(r - s)(r + s)$ _____

13. $(p - q) - r$ _____

14. $m(p - q)$ _____

15. $(x + y) - ks$ _____

16. $r - pq$ _____

Name _____

Date _____ Period _____

Translate each sentence into an equation. Use *n* to represent the number.

1. The sum of a number and 7 is 35. $n + 7 = 35$

2. Five more than a number is 17.

3. Five is 6 less than twice a number.

4. If seven is subtracted from six times a number, the result is 10.

5. Ten more than a number is 62.

6. The product of three times a number and twelve is twenty.

7. One-half of a number equals sixteen.

8. The sum of a number and thirteen is 22.

9. The sum of four and twice a number is 52.

10. Ten times a number is 420.

11. Five times a number is 120.

12. The sum of five and twice a number is 17.

13. If 3 times a number is decreased by 12, the result is 5.

14. Five more than a number is seventeen.

15. The product of 6 times a number and fifteen is forty-two.

16. If 5 times a number is decreased by 12, the difference is 9.

Name _____

Date _____ Period _____

Translate each sentence into an equation. Use *n* to represent the number.

1. One-third of a number is 12 less than the number itself. $\frac{1}{3}n = n - 12$

2. Twice a number divided by 6 is 42.

3. Four less than a number, multiplied by 6, is 25.

4. One-half of a number is 7 less than the number itself.

5. Forty-five divided by a number is 5.

6. Seven more than one-third of a number is 15.

7. Five more than one-third of a number is 18.

8. Nine less than 3 times a number, divided by four, is 21.

9. Twice a number divided by 4 is 25.

10. Twelve more than a number, divided by 3, is 9.

11. The sum of a number and 3, divided by 5, is 2 more than the number.

12. Sixteen more than five times a number is 24.

13. Six more than one-fourth of a number is 15.

14. Five times two less than a number equals seventeen.

15. If the sum of a number and 7 is divided by 2, the result is 19.

16. If the sum of a number and 7 is divided by 4, the result is 19 more than the number.

Number Problems

Name _____

Date _____ Period _____

Write an equation and solve.

1. Four less than a number is 172. Find the number. $n - 4 = 172$
$n = 176$

2. Ten more than a number is −122. Find the number.

3. Twenty-two more than a number is −105. Find the number.

4. Twelve less than a number is 114. Find the number.

5. If seventeen is subtracted from a number, the result is 35. Find the number.

6. Forty-six less than a number is 78. Find the number.

7. Twenty-two more than a number is 47. Find the number.

8. Fifty-six more than a number is 82. Find the number.

9. Twelve more than a number is 67. Find the number.

10. Sixteen more than a number is 59. Find the number.

11. Fifty-two more than a number is −11. Find the number.

12. Eighty-five more than a number is −34. Find the number.

13. Four more than a number is 15. Find the number.

14. Seven more than a number is 17. Find the number.

15. Six less than a number is 22. Find the number.

16. Twelve less than a number is −14. Find the number.

Developing Skills in Algebra   Book A

Name _____

Date _____ Period _____

Write an equation and solve.

1. Seven less than a number is 114. Find the number. $n - 7 = 114$
$n = 121$

2. Four more than a number is -95. Find the number.

3. Thirty-five more than a number is -116. Find the number.

4. Eighteen less than a number is 76. Find the number.

5. If eleven is subtracted from a number, the result is 28. Find the number.

6. Fifty-five less than a number is -16. Find the number.

7. Forty-seven more than a number is 51. Find the number.

8. Nineteen more than a number is 51. Find the number.

9. Twenty more than a number is -12. Find the number.

10. Thirty-two more than a number is 75. Find the number.

11. Seventy-five more than a number is -106. Find the number.

12. Twenty-three more than a number is -45. Find the number.

13. Fifty more than a number is 13. Find the number.

14. Twenty-nine more than a number is 15. Find the number.

15. Nine less than a number is 53. Find the number.

16. Sixteen less than a number is -27. Find the number.

92

Name _____

Date _____ Period _____

Write an equation and solve.

1. Four times a number equals 28. Find the number.

$$4w = 28$$
$$w = 7$$

2. Six times a number equals −36. Find the number.

3. One-half of a number is seventeen. Find the number.

4. Two-thirds of a number is −12. Find the number.

5. Seven times a number equals −77. Find the number.

6. Eight times a number is 44. Find the number.

7. Jerry is twice as old as Mary. If Jerry is twelve years old, how old is Mary?

8. John is four times as old as his son. If John is 44 years old, how old is his son?

9. The length of a rectangle is four times the width. If the length is 20 inches, what is the width?

10. The length of a rectangle is six times the width. If the length is 18 inches, what is the width?

11. Two-thirds of the students in class are male. If 18 of the students are male, how many students are in the class?

12. Three-fourths of the student body attended the pep rally. If there were 1230 at the pep rally, how many students are there in all?

13. If $\frac{5}{8}$ yard of fabric costs $3.75, what does one yard cost?

14. If $\frac{3}{4}$ pound of coffee costs $3.90, what does one pound cost?

Name _____

Date _____ Period _____

Write an equation and solve.

1. Seven times a number equals 63. Find the number. $7n = 63$
$n = 9$

2. Nine times a number equals 72. Find the number.

3. One-half of a number is fifteen. Find the number.

4. Two-thirds of a number is -32. Find the number.

5. Five times a number equals 100. Find the number.

6. Twelve times a number is -108. Find the number.

7. Ann is twice as old as Harry. If Ann is eighteen years old, how old is Harry?

8. Philip is three times as old as his son. If Philip is 45 years old, how old is his son?

9. The length of a rectangle is five times the width. If the length is 20 inches, what is the width?

10. The length of a rectangle is eight times the width. If the length is 24 inches, what is the width?

11. Three-fifths of the students in class are boys. If 21 of the students are boys, how many students are in the class?

12. Two-thirds of the student body attended the pep rally. If there were 982 at the pep rally, how many students are there in all?

13. If $\frac{7}{8}$ yard of fabric costs $8.75, what does one yard cost?

14. If $\frac{2}{3}$ pound of coffee costs $4.84, what does one pound cost?

Developing Skills in Algebra   Book A

Name _____

Date _____ Period _____

Show a complete solution for each problem.

1. Two cars start at the same place but travel in opposite directions. One car averages 42 miles per hour and the other averages 51 miles per hour. How many hours will it be before the cars are 651 miles apart?

   distance first car + distance second car = 651

   Let t =
   number of hours
   traveled

   $$42t \quad + \quad 51t \qquad\qquad = 651$$
   $$93t = 651$$
   $$t = 7$$

2. Two cars travel in opposite directions, starting from the same place at the same time. One travels at an average rate of 48 miles per hour and the other averages at 55 miles per hour. In how many hours will they be 618 miles apart?

3. Two trains start at the same place, traveling in opposite directions for 6 hours. After 3 hours they are 414 miles apart. How fast is each traveling if the rate of one train is 8 miles per hour faster than the other?

4. Two trains travel for eleven hours, starting from the same place traveling in opposite directions. One train travels at an average rate that is 11 miles per hour faster than the other one. Find the rate of each train if they are 635 miles apart after five hours.

5. Two airplanes start at the same place and travel in opposite directions, one at 520 miles per hour and the other at 448 miles per hour. How many hours will it take for them to be 1936 miles apart?

6. Two airplanes leave the same place and fly in opposite directions. The average rate of one plane is 18 miles per hour faster than the other one. Find the rate of each plane if they are 1179 miles apart after $1\frac{1}{2}$ hours.

7. One car travels 50 miles per hour and another one travels 55 miles per hour. If they start from the same place at the same time and travel in the same direction, after how many hours will the faster car be 35 miles ahead of the slower car?

8. One car travels 62 miles per hour and another travels 48 miles per hour. If they start from the same place at the same time and travel in the same direction, after how many hours will the faster car be 42 miles ahead of the slower one?

Name _____

Date _____ Period _____

Show a complete solution for each problem.

1. Two cars start at the same place but travel in opposite directions. One car averages 53 miles per hour and the other averages 59 miles per hour. How many hours will it be before the cars are 896 miles apart? *Let t = number of hours traveled*

   distance first car + distance second car = 896

   $$53t + 59t = 896$$
   $$= 896$$
   $$112t = 896$$
   $$t = 8$$

2. Two cars travel in opposite directions, starting from the same place at the same time. One travels at an average rate of 43 miles per hour and the other averages at 38 miles per hour. In how many hours will they be 405 miles apart?

3. Two trains start at the same place, traveling in opposite directions for 6 hours. After 4 hours they are 424 miles apart. How fast is each traveling if the rate of one train is 10 miles per hour faster than the other train?

4. Two trains travel for eleven hours, starting from the same place traveling in opposite directions. One train travels at an average rate that is 15 miles per hour faster than the other train. Find the rate of each train if they are 291 miles apart after three hours.

5. Two airplanes start at the same place and travel in opposite directions, one at 395 miles per hour and the other at 422 miles per hour. How many hours will it take for the planes to be 2451 miles apart?

6. Two airplanes leave the same place and fly in opposite directions. The average rate of one plane is 32 miles per hour faster than the other one. Find the rate of each plane if they are 1098 miles apart after $1\frac{1}{2}$ hours.

7. One car travels 45 miles per hour and another one travels 52 miles per hour. If they start from the same place at the same time, traveling in the same direction, after how many hours will the faster car be 42 miles ahead of the slower one?

8. One car travels 56 miles per hour and another travels 31 miles per hour. If they start from the same place at the same time and travel in the same direction, after how many hours will the faster car be 75 miles ahead of the slower car?

Motion Problems   Name _____

                                                        Date _____ Period _____

_____

Show a complete solution for each problem.

1. Mr. James drove his car from San Francisco to San Diego at an average rate of 50 miles per hour and returned at an average rate of 60 miles per hour. Find his time going and returning if the time returning was one hour less than the time going.

$t =$ time going
$t - 1 =$ time returning

distance going = distance returning
$50t = 60(t-1)$
$50t = 60t - 60$
$10t = 60$
$t = 6$ $t - 1 = 5$

2. Marilyn drove her car from Amarillo to Dallas at an average rate of 55 miles per hour and returned over icy roads averaging only 30 miles per hour. Find the time going and returning if the time returning was 4 hours more than the time going.

3. Two freight trains started at the same time from towns 564 miles apart and met in six hours. The average rate of one train was 14 miles per hour faster than that of the other train. Find the rate of each train.

4. Two passenger trains started at the same time from towns 608 miles apart and met in 4 hours. The rate of one train was 8 miles per hour slower than that of the other. Find the rate of each train.

5. Jose left Westcliffe on his bicycle riding at an average rate of 8 miles per hour five hours before his father left by automobile. The father overtook Jose in exactly one hour. At what average rate was Jose's father traveling?

6. Lysa left camp on her bicycle at noon and rode at an average rate of 10 miles per hour. Morton left camp in his van at 1:30 P.M. and overtook Lysa in 30 minutes. At what average rate was he traveling in the van?

7. Maya averaged 16 miles per hour in a boat traveling downstream and 6 miles per hour traveling upstream. She traveled a total of 44 miles spending as much time going downstream as upstream. How long did she spend going in each direction?

8. Norman started across a lake 10 miles wide in his fishing boat at 12 miles per hour. After his motor went out, he had to row the rest of the way at only 3 miles per hour. If he was rowing for half the time that the total trip took, how long did the total trip take?

Name _____

Date _____ Period _____

Show a complete solution for each problem.

1. Mr. Howard drove his car from Los Angeles to Sacramento at an average rate of 52 miles per hour and returned at an average rate of 57 miles per hour. Find his time going and returning if the time returning was one hour less than the time going.

$t = $ time going

$t - 1 = $ time returning

distance going = distance returning

$52 t = 57(t - 1)$

$52t = 57t - 57$

$5t = 57$

$t = 11.4 \qquad t - 1 = 10.4$

2. Marilyn drove her car from Lubbock to Houston at an average rate of 48 miles per hour and returned over icy roads averaging only 28 miles per hour. Find the time going and returning if the time returning was 5 hours more than the time going.

3. Two freight trains started at the same time from towns 448 miles apart and met in 8 hours. The average rate of one train was 19 miles per hour faster than that of the other train. Find the rate of each train.

4. Two passenger trains started at the same time from towns 288 miles apart and met in 3 hours. The rate of one train was 6 miles per hour slower than that of the other. Find the rate of each train.

5. Albert left Westcliffe on his bicycle riding at an average rate of 10 miles per hour three hours before his son left by automobile. The son overtook Albert in exactly 30 minutes. At what average rate was Albert's son traveling?

6. Sue left camp on her bicycle at 2 P.M. and rode at an average rate of 8 miles per hour. Tom left camp in his van at 3:30 P.M. and overtook Sue in 15 minutes. At what average rate was he traveling in the van?

7. Ty averaged 13 miles per hour in a boat traveling downstream and 7 miles per hour traveling upstream. He traveled a total of 60 miles spending as much time going downstream as upstream. How long did he spend going in each direction?

8. David started across a lake 15 miles wide in his fishing boat at 10 miles per hour. He had to row the rest of the way at only 5 miles per hour after his motor went out. If he was rowing for half the time that the total trip took, how long did the total trip take?

Developing Skills in Algebra   Book A

Consecutive Integer Problems   Name _____

                                      Date _____ Period _____

_____

Show a complete solution for each problem.

1. The sum of three consecutive integers is 105. Find the integers.

$x = $ first integer $x + (x+1) + (x+2) = 105$
$x + 1 = $ second integer $3x + 3 = 105$
$x + 2 = $ third integer $3x = 102$
                                                    $x = 34$ $x+1 = 35$ $x+2 = 36$

2. The sum of three consecutive integers is -129. Find the integers.

3. The sum of four consecutive integers is -334. Find the integers.

4. The sum of four consecutive integers is 262. Find the integers.

5. The sum of three consecutive integers is 33 more than the least of the integers. Find the integers.

6. The sum of three consecutive integers is 47 less than the least of the integers. Find the integers.

7. The sum of three consecutive even integers is 138. Find the integers.

8. The sum of three consecutive even integers is -312. Find the integers.

9. The sum of three consecutive odd integers is -219. Find the integers.

10. The sum of three consecutive odd integers is 285. Find the integers.

11. The sum of four consecutive even integers is the same as the least of the integers. Find the integers.

12. The sum of four consecutive odd integers is 0. Find the integers.

Consecutive Integer Problems   Name _____

                                                Date _____ Period _____

Show a complete solution for each problem.

1. The sum of three consecutive integers is 138. Find the integers.

   $x = $ first integer $x + (x+1) + (x+2) = 138$
   $x+1 = $ second integer $3x + 3 = 138$
   $x+2 = $ third integer $3x = 135$
                                           $x = 45$ $x+1 = 46$ $x+2 = 47$

2. The sum of three consecutive integers is -114. Find the integers.

3. The sum of four consecutive integers is -294. Find the integers.

4. The sum of four consecutive integers is 238. Find the integers.

5. The sum of three consecutive integers is 53 more than the least of the integers. Find the integers.

6. The sum of three consecutive integers is 71 less than the least of the integers. Find the integers.

7. The sum of three consecutive even integers is 210. Find the integers.

8. The sum of three consecutive even integers is -360. Find the integers.

9. The sum of three consecutive odd integers is 111. Find the integers.

10. The sum of three consecutive odd integers is -75. Find the integers.

11. The sum of four consecutive even integers equals seven times the greatest of the integers. Find the integers.

12. The sum of four consecutive odd integers is three more than five times the least of the integers. Find the integers.

Problem Solving With Equations

Name _____

Date _____ Period _____

Show a complete solution for each problem.

1. Separate 126 into two parts so that one part is 16 more than the other part. Find each part.

$x = $ one part $x + (x+16) = 126$
$x + 16 = $ other part $2x + 16 = 126$
       $2x = 110$
       $x = 55$ $x + 16 = 71$

2. Separate 185 into two parts so that one part is 31 more than the other part. Find each part.

3. Separate 46 into two parts so that one part is one more than twice as much as the first part. Find each part.

4. Separate 77 into two parts so that one part is 4 less than twice as much as the other. Find each part.

5. A board 76 inches long is to be cut into two parts so that one part is 5 inches less than twice as long as the other part. Find the length of each part.

6. A board 109 cm long is to be cut into two pieces so that the longer part is 10 cm more than twice as long as the shorter part. Find the length of each part.

7. Rhonda worked three more than twice as many hours as Ron did. How many hours did each work if together they worked 57 hours?

8. Jim worked five less than twice as many hours as Jane did. How many hours did each work if together they worked 97 hours?

9. The sum of the ages of Jerry and his father is 64 years. The difference in their ages is 32 years. How old is each?

10. The sum of the ages of Ruth and her mother is 77 years. The difference in their ages is 27 years. How old is each?

11. The sum of $224 was divided among 3 people so that the second person received $1 less than twice as much as the first, and the third received $11 more than the second. How much did each person receive?

12. The sum of $127 was divided among 3 people so that the second received $5 less than twice as much as the first, and the third received $2 more than the second. How much did each person receive?

Problem Solving With Equations   Name _____

                                             Date _____ Period _____

Show a complete solution for each problem.

1. Separate 90 into two parts so that one part is 16 more than the other part. Find each part.

$x =$ one part $x + (x + 16) = 90$
$x + 16 =$ other part $2x + 16 = 90$
                          $2x = 74$ $x + 16 = 53$
                          $x = 37$

2. Separate 104 into two parts so that one part is 18 more than the other part. Find each part.

3. Separate 72 into two parts so that one part is 3 more than twice as much as the first part. Find each part.

4. Separate 84 into two parts so that one part is 9 less than twice as much as the other. Find each part.

5. A board 125 inches long is to be cut into two parts so that one part is 4 inches less than twice as long as the other part. Find the length of each part.

6. A board 91 cm long is to be cut into two pieces so that the longer part is 10 cm more than twice as long as the shorter part. Find the length of each part.

7. Connie worked three more than twice as many hours as Gary did. How many hours did each work if together they worked 48 hours?

8. Stanley worked 6 more than twice as many hours as Kathleen did. How many hours did each work if together they worked 69 hours?

9. The sum of the ages of Rudy and his father is 58 years. The difference in their ages is 32 years. How old is each?

10. The sum of the ages of Ruth and her mother is 75 years. The difference in their ages is 29 years. How old is each?

11. The sum of $180 was divided among 3 people so that the second person received $6 less than twice as much as the first, and the third received $7 more than the second. How much did each person receive?

12. The sum of $305 was divided among 3 people so that the second received $4 less than twice as much as the first, and the third received $23 more than the second. How much did each person receive?

102   Developing Skills in Algebra   Book A

Coin Problems

Name _____

Date _____ Period _____

Show a complete solution for each problem.

1. Mr. Chen put $4.75 in quarters in a pay telephone. How many quarters was this?

q = number of quarters $0.25q = 4.75$
$q = 19$

2. Mr. Lawson put $7.25 in quarters in a bridge toll box during the period of one month. How many quarters was this?

3. Yolanda had three times as many nickels as dimes. If the total value of her coins was $1, how many of each kind of coin did she have?

4. Eugenia had five times as many quarters as dimes. If the total value of her coins was $16.20, how many of each kind of coin did she have?

5. A cash box contained $14.55 in quarters, dimes, and nickels. If there were three more than twice as many dimes as nickels and three less than three times as many quarters as nickels, how many of each kind of coin was there?

6. Ginny's piggybank contained $8.80 in quarters, dimes, and nickels. There were two more than five times as many nickels as quarters and 4 less than twice as many dimes as quarters. How many of each kind of coin was there in the bank?

7. Lupe, who works at a fast food restaurant received $6.10 in tips one afternoon, all in quarters, dimes, and nickels. There were five less dimes than quarters and seven less nickels than dimes. How many of each kind of coin was there?

8. A valuable collection of coins contained old nickels, dimes, quarters, and pennies. The face value of the pennies was $6. There were five times as many quarters as dimes and fifteen less than twice as many nickels as quarters. If the face value of the entire collection was $40.40, how many of each kind of coin was there?

Coin Problems

Name _____

Date _____ Period _____

Show a complete solution for each problem.

1. Mr. Wills put $5.50 in quarters in a pay telephone. How many quarters was this?

$q = $ *number of quarters* $0.25q = 5.50$

$q = 22$

2. Mr. Anderson put $9.25 in quarters in a bridge toll box during the period of one month. How many quarters was this?

3. Josiah had three less than twice as many nickels as dimes. If the total value of his coins was $1.45, how many of each kind of coin did he have?

4. Mary Ann had 7 more than twice as many quarters as dimes. If the total value of her coins was $10.15, how many of each kind of coin did she have?

5. A cash box contained $12.25 in quarters, dimes, and nickels. If there were five more than twice as many dimes as nickels and one less than three times as many quarters as nickels, how many of each kind of coin was there?

6. Vera's piggybank contained $9.35 in quarters, dimes, and nickels. There were six more than two times as many nickels as quarters and four less dimes than quarters. How many of each kind of coin was there in the bank?

7. Rosa, who works at a fast food restaurant, received $9.05 in tips one afternoon, all in quarters, dimes, and nickels. There were ten less dimes than quarters and five less nickels than dimes. How many of each kind of coin was there?

8. A valuable collection of coins contained old nickels, dimes, quarters, and pennies. The face value of the pennies was $8. There were seven more than three times as many quarters as dimes and sixteen less than twice as many nickels as quarters. If the face value of the entire collection was $38.40, how many of each kind of coin was there?

Angle Problems

Name _____

Date _____ Period _____

Show a complete solution for each problem.

The sum of the degree measures of two complementary angles is 90.

1. If the measure of one of two complementary angles is 12 less than twice the measure of the other, find the measure of each angle.

    a = measure of one angle

    $2a - 12$ = measure of other angle

    $$a + (2a - 12) = 90$$
    $$3a - 12 = 90$$
    $$3a = 102$$
    $$a = 34 \qquad 2a - 12 = 56$$

2. If the measure of one of two complementary angles is 22 more than three times the measure of the other, find the measure of each angle.

The sum of the degree measures of two supplementary angles is 180.

3. If the measure of one of two supplementary angles is five less than four times the measure of the other, find the measure of each angle.

4. If the measure of one of two supplementary angles is eight less than three times the measure of the other, find the measure of each angle.

The sum of the degree measures of the angles of a triangle is 180.

5. The second angle of a triangle measures three less than twice that of the first angle and the third angle measures eight more than twice that of the first. Find the measure of each angle.

6. Two of the angles of a triangle have the same measure and the third angle measures 15 more than each of the other two. Find the measure of each angle.

Consecutive angles of a parallelogram are supplementary.

7. One of two consecutive angles of a parallelogram measures six more than twice as much as the other. Find the measures of the angles.

8. One of two consecutive angles of a parallelogram measures 16 less than three times as much as the other. Find the measure of each angle.

Angle Problems

Name _____

Date _____ Period _____

Show a complete solution for each problem.

The sum of the degree measures of two complementary angles is 90.

1. If the measure of one of two complementary angles is three more than twice the measure of the other, find the measure of each angle.

   a = measure of one angle
   $2a + 3$ = measure of other angle

   $a + (2a + 3) = 90$
   $3a + 3 = 90$
   $3a = 87$
   $a = 29$ $2a+3 = 61$

2. If the measure of one of two complementary angles is 21 less than twice the measure of the other, find the measure of each angle.

The sum of the degree measures of two supplementary angles is 180.

3. If the measure of one of two supplementary angles is twelve less than three times the measure of the other, find the measure of each angle.

4. If the measure of one of two supplementary angles is six less than five times the measure of the other, find the measure of each angle.

The sum of the degree measures of the angles of a triangle is 180.

5. The second angle of a triangle measures seven more than twice that of the first angle and the third angle measures five more than three times that of the first. Find the measure of each angle.

6. Two of the angles of a triangle have the same measure and the third angle measures twice that of each of the other two. Find the measure of each angle.

Consecutive angles of a parallelogram are supplementary.

7. One of two consecutive angles of a parallelogram measures eight less than three times as much as the other. Find the measures of the angles.

8. One of two consecutive angles of a parallelogram measures nine less than twice as much as the other. Find the measure of each angle.

ANSWERS

Page 1   Simplifying Numerical Expressions

1. 1 **2.** 1.6 **3.** 1 **4.** 192 **5.** 1 **6.** 1 **7.** 1 **8.** 0 **9.** 1
10. 4 **11.** 1 **12.** 2 **13.** 16 **14.** 24 **15.** 58 **16.** 72
17. F **18.** T **19.** T **20.** T **21.** T **22.** F **23.** T **24.** F
25. F **26.** T **27.** T **28.** F **29.** F **30.** F **31.** T **32.** F

Page 2   Simplifying Numerical Expressions

1. 16 **2.** 625 **3.** 221 **4.** 800 **5.** 13 **6.** 15 **7.** 18 **8.** 20
9. 6000 **10.** 1024 **11.** 13 **12.** 9 **13.** 243 **14.** 32
15. 14 **16.** 1151 **17.** T **18.** F **19.** T **20.** T **21.** T
22. F **23.** F **24.** T **25.** F **26.** F **27.** T **28.** T
29. F **30.** F **31.** T **32.** T

Page 3   Simplifying Numerical Expressions

1. 2, 34 **2.** 2, 14 **3.** 3, 35 **4.** 2, 25 **5.** 2, 12 **6.** 3, 31
7. 3, 17 **8.** 3, 8 **9.** 35 **10.** 44 **11.** 39 **12.** 46 **13.** 53
14. 27 **15.** 57 **16.** 80 **17.** 27 **18.** 11 **19.** 52
20. 7 **21.** 3, 42 **22.** 4, 816 **23.** 4, 2925 **24.** 3, 630
25. 2, 187 **26.** 3, 6624 **27.** 4, 45849 **28.** 2, 118
29. 2, 215 **30.** 3, 648

Page 4   Simplifying Numerical Expressions

1. 2, 61 **2.** 2, 0 **3.** 3, 54 **4.** 2, 97 **5.** 2, 14 **6.** 3, 26
7. 3, 27 **8.** 3, 11 **9.** 53 **10.** 36 **11.** 59 **12.** 64 **13.** 58
14. 39 **15.** 18 **16.** 64 **17.** 30 **18.** 21 **19.** 57
20. 18 **21.** 4, 270 **22.** 3, 390 **23.** 3, 225 **24.** 4, 1008
25. 2, 315 **26.** 4, 22320 **27.** 3, 1008 **28.** 3, 4080
29. 3, 2024 **30.** 3, 320

Page 5   Evaluating Variable Expressions

1. 15 **2.** 8 **3.** 70 **4.** 2 **5.** 41 **6.** 15 **7.** 122 **8.** 105
9. 45 **10.** 3 **11.** 26 **12.** 9 **13.** 0 **14.** 2 **15.** 216
16. 21 **17.** 18 **18.** 14 **19.** 42 **20.** 33 **21.** 16 **22.** 2
23. 4 **24.** 32 **25.** 1 **26.** 2 **27.** 21 **28.** 3 **29.** 45
30. 1

Page 6   Evaluating Variable Expressions

1. 20 **2.** 1 **3.** 40 **4.** 32 **5.** 20 **6.** 60 **7.** 107 **8.** 124
9. 105 **10.** 7 **11.** 44 **12.** 75 **13.** 6 **14.** 6 **15.** 46
16. 105 **17.** 2 **18.** 28 **19.** 12 **20.** 4 **21.** 3 **22.** 26
23. 47 **24.** 7 **25.** 8 **26.** 2 **27.** 3 **28.** 1 **29.** 10
30. 36

Page 7   Using Formulas

1. 75, 40 **2.** 434, 138 **3.** 1000, 220 **4.** 20000, 600
5. 37500, 800 **6.** 10875, 440 **7.** 25, 20 **8.** 49, 28
9. 100, 40 **10.** 676, 104 **11.** 5929, 308 **12.** 2704, 208
13. 6, 12 **14.** 30, 30 **15.** 60, 40 **16.** 159 1/2, 71
17. 120, 60 **18.** 84, 56

Page 8   Using Formulas

1. 28, 24 **2.** 112, 48 **3.** 228, 68 **4.** 384, 88
5. 620, 112 **6.** 252, 76 **7.** 5, 14 **8.** 21, 22 **9.** 32, 26
10. 50, 34 **11.** 48, 36 **12.** 198, 66 **13.** 154, 44
14. 1386, 132 **15.** 616, 88 **16.** 2464, 176
17. 38 1/2, 22 **18.** 98.56, 35.2

Page 9   Exponents

1. a^7 **2.** c^5 **3.** a^2b^4 **4.** a^4b^3 **5.** $a^2b^2c^3$ **6.** a^3bc^4
7. $3x^2y^3z$ **8.** $7xy^4z^2$ **9.** $4xxyy$ **10.** $10xxxyyz$
11. $3aaabbc$ **12.** $5aabbbcc$ **13.** $2mmmmn$ **14.** $9rrrssstt$
15. $7bcccc$ **16.** $13ppppq$ **17.** $48aaabb$ **18.** $10xxxxxxxy$
19. $10xxxxxyyyyy$ **20.** $42aaaaaabbbb$
21. $48mmmmnnnn$ **22.** $28rrrrrssssstt$ **23.** 2240
24. 16000 **25.** 5120 **26.** 115200 **27.** 704
28. 6000 **29.** 960 **30.** 12800

Page 10   Exponents

1. m^5 **2.** r^7 **3.** x^3y^3 **4.** c^2d^5 **5.** m^3n^2 **6.** r^2s^3t **7.** $6mn^4$
8. $5a^4b^2c^2$ **9.** $2mmnn$ **10.** $12aaabbcc$ **11.** $5xxxyyz$
12. $9rrssstt$ **13.** $4aabbbcccc$ **14.** $8ppqqqq$
15. $9mmmnn$ **16.** $18ccddd$ **17.** $12xxxyyy$
18. $168mmmmmnnnn$ **19.** $21aaaaaabbbbb$
20. $12cccccddddd$ **21.** $60rrrrsssss$
22. $80aaaaabbbbbcccc$ **23.** 576 **24.** 12096 **25.** 2880
26. 9216 **27.** 13608 **28.** 2304 **29.** 108 **30.** 6048

Page 11   Evaluating Formulas

1. 27, 54 **2.** 343, 294 **3.** 125, 150 **4.** 729, 486
5. 3375, 1350 **6.** 1331, 726 **7.** 30, 62 **8.** 360, 332
9. 154, 226 **10.** 520, 418 **11.** 858, 574 **12.** 2772, 1440
13. 6930, 660 **14.** 3564, 792 **15.** 7986, 1452
16. 7040, 1760 **17.** 12672, 2112 **18.** 2112, 1056

Page 12   Evaluating Formulas

1. 47 **2.** 103 **3.** 19.1 **4.** 1.12 **5.** 50 **6.** 41 **7.** $548.80
8. $367.20 **9.** $286.56 **10.** $571.50 **11.** $1366.56
12. $1306.62 **13.** 385 mi **14.** 1140 mi **15.** 376 mi/h
16. 732 mi/h **17.** 13 h **18.** 17 h

Page 13   Grouping Symbols

1. 2 **2.** 4 **3.** 14 **4.** 21 **5.** 10 **6.** 15 **7.** 14 **8.** 20
9. 14 **10.** 20 **11.** 20 **12.** 57 **13.** 40 **14.** 120
15. 8 **16.** 21 **17.** 8 **18.** 2 **19.** 15 **20.** 8 **21.** 1 **22.** 6
23. 6 **24.** 13 **25.** 2 **26.** 3 **27.** 29 **28.** 47 **29.** 13
30. 75 **31.** 3 **32.** 8 **33.** 5 **34.** 2

Page 14   Grouping Symbols

1. 7 **2.** 5 **3.** 11 **4.** 28 **5.** 9 **6.** 20 **7.** 21 **8.** 39
9. 22 **10.** 39 **11.** 34 **12.** 92 **13.** 70 **14.** 176 **15.** 3
16. 20 **17.** 13 **18.** 22 **19.** 7 **20.** 5 **21.** 1 **22.** 18
23. 5 **24.** 13 **25.** 2 **26.** 1 **27.** 72 **28.** 55 **29.** 16
30. 70 **31.** 8 **32.** 14 **33.** 6 **34.** 3

Page 15   Inserting Parentheses

1. 11 **2.** 44 **3.** 16 **4.** 48 **5.** 22 **6.** 38 **7.** 16 **8.** 14
9. 10 **10.** 9 **11.** 4 **12.** 5 **13.** 3 **14.** 2 **15.** 4 **16.** 36
17. $10 \cdot (2 + 3) = 50$ **18.** $(17 \cdot 3) + 6 = 57$
19. $(10 \cdot 2) + 3 = 23$ **20.** $17 \cdot (3 + 6) = 153$
21. $(19 \cdot 2) + 3 = 41$ **22.** $(72 \div 12) \div 2 = 3$
23. $19 \cdot (2 + 3) = 95$ **24.** $72 \div (12 \div 2) = 12$
25. $(56 \div 7) \div 2 = 4$ **26.** $100 \div (10 \div 10) = 100$
27. $4 \cdot (8 - 8) = 0$ **28.** $(36 \div 3) + 8 = 20$
29. $(26 \div 13) - 2 = 0$ **30.** $26 \cdot (4 - 4) = 0$
31. $(41 - 35) \div 6 = 1$ **32.** $(52 - 7) \div 9 = 5$

Page 16 Inserting Parentheses

1. 36 **2.** 42 **3.** 60 **4.** 162 **5.** 17 **6.** 42 **7.** 5 **8.** 18
9. 15 **10.** 18 **11.** 7 **12.** 8 **13.** 3 **14.** 10 **15.** 95 **16.** 180
17. 19 · (5 + 2) = 133 **18.** (24 · 8) + 5 = 197
19. (19 · 5) + 2 = 97 **20.** 24 · (8 + 5) = 312
21. (35 · 7) + 9 = 254 **22.** (200 ÷ 4) ÷ 2 = 25
23. 35 · (7 + 9) = 560 **24.** 100 ÷ (4 ÷ 2) = 50
25. (63 ÷ 7) ÷ 3 = 3 **26.** 250 ÷ (10 ÷ 5) = 125
27. (6 · 3) – 12 = 6 **28.** (49 ÷ 7) + 8 = 15
29. (52 ÷ 26) + 2 = 4 **30.** 99 – (33 ÷ 3) = 88
31. 84 ÷ (6 ÷ 2) = 28 **32.** (52 ÷ 26) ÷ 2 = 1

Page 17 Grouping Symbols

1. 2 **2.** 2 **3.** 10 **4.** 70 **5.** 22 **6.** 53 **7.** 54 **8.** 203
9. 16 **10.** 23 **11.** 12 **12.** 11 **13.** 8 **14.** 4 **15.** 56
16. 154 **17.** 8 **18.** 13 **19.** 2 **20.** 4 **21.** 21 **22.** 24
23. 5 **24.** 0 **25.** 90 **26.** 136 **27.** 210 **28.** 406 **29.** 342
30. 1134 **31.** 222 **32.** 864

Page 18 Grouping Symbols

1. 3 **2.** 15 **3.** 12 **4.** 40 **5.** 32 **6.** 47 **7.** 80 **8.** 222
9. 53 **10.** 63 **11.** 23 **12.** 21 **13.** 120 **14.** 21 **15.** 504
16. 225 **17.** 376 **18.** 69 **19.** 61 **20.** 21 **21.** 1510
22. 1986 **23.** 124 **24.** 218 **25.** 17 **26.** 94 **27.** 9 1/2
28. 34 **29.** 12 **30.** 30 **31.** 20 **32.** 270/7 or 38 4/7

Page 19 Directed Distance

1. +, 4 **2.** –, 9 **3.** +, 3 **4.** –, 3 **5.** –, 3 **6.** +, 10
7. +, 10 **8.** –, 10 **9.** –, 5 **10.** –, 12 **11.** +2 **12.** –6
13. +8 **14.** –10 **15.** 0 **16.** –11 **17.** +11 **18.** +5
19. –10 **20.** -8 **21.** +9 **22.** -6 **23.** < **24.** < **25.** >
26. > **27.** < **28.** <

Page 20 Directed Distance

1. –, 7 **2.** +, 7 **3.** –, 3 **4.** –, 7 **5.** +, 6 **6.** –, 7 **7.** +,
8 **8.** +, 15 **9.** –, 24 **10.** +, 11 **11.** –2 **12.** –15
13. +14 **14.** –5 **15.** +3 **16.** –21 **17.** +25 **18.** –15
19. –16 **20.** –24 **21.** +9 **22.** 0 **23.** < **24.** > **25.** <
26. > **27.** > **28.** >

Page 21 Graphing Integers

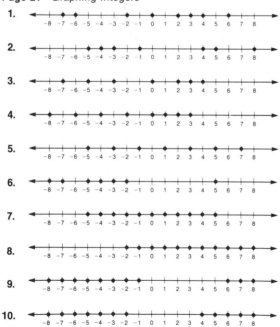

Page 22 Graphing Integers

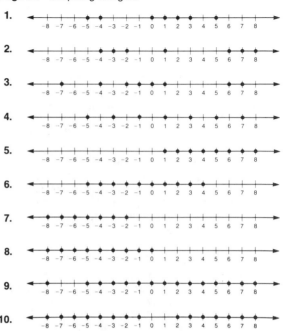

Page 23 Absolute Value

1. 5 **2.** 5 **3.** 10 **4.** 12 **5.** 43 **6.** 17 **7.** 10 **8.** 11 **9.** 10
10. 47 **11.** 2 **12.** 12 **13.** 7 **14.** 18 **15.** 21 **16.** 27
17. 35 **18.** 49 **19.** {18, –18} **20.** {9, –9} **21.** {22, –22}
22. ∅ **23.** {30, –30} **24.** {13, –13} **25.** {44, –44}
26. {29, –29} **27.** {62, –62} **28.** {0} **29.** ∅ **30.** {11, –11}

Page 24 Absolute Value

1. 7 **2.** 7 **3.** 22 **4.** 14 **5.** 75 **6.** 63 **7.** 14 **8.** 16 **9.** 21
10. 58 **11.** 2 **12.** 3 **13.** 34 **14.** 45 **15.** 10 **16.** 38
17. 15 **18.** 10 **19.** {5, –5} **20.** {12, –12} **21.** ∅
22. {21, –21} **23.** {0} **24.** {25, –25} **25.** {31, –31} **26.** ∅
27. {99, –99} **28.** {17, –17} **29.** {10, –10} **30.** {42, –42}

Page 25 Absolute Value

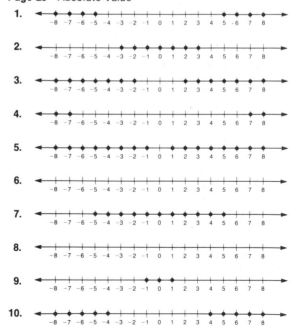

Page 26 Absolute Value

1.
2.
3.
4.
5.
6.
7.
8.
9.
10.

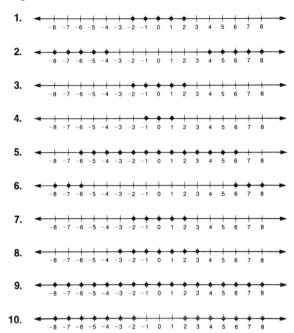

Page 27 Addition of Integers

1. -2 **2.** 4 **3.** -5 **4.** -4 **5.** 0 **6.** -5 **7.** 1 **8.** -11
9. -13 **10.** -8 **11.** -1 **12.** 5 **13.** 13 **14.** 3 **15.** 3
16. -11 **17.** -6 **18.** -16 **19.** 4 **20.** 2 **21.** -9
22. 0 **23.** 13 **24.** 4 **25.** -6 **26.** 18 **27.** 0 **28.** -18
29. -5 **30.** -4

Page 28 Addition of Integers

1. 6 **2.** -17 **3.** -14 **4.** 2 **5.** 5 **6.** -6 **7.** -4
8. -10 **9.** 0 **10.** 2 **11.** 1 **12.** -14 **13.** 15 **14.** 14
15. -2 **16.** 0 **17.** 2 **18.** -13 **19.** -6 **20.** 4 **21.** -10
22. 9 **23.** -9 **24.** 13 **25.** -16 **26.** -23 **27.** 6 **28.** -15
29. -8 **30.** -10

Page 29 Addition of Integers

1. 21 **2.** 14 **3.** 19 **4.** -64 **5.** 2 **6.** 8 **7.** 16 **8.** 15
9. -36 **10.** -71 **11.** 23 **12.** 26 **13.** -16 **14.** -2
15. -20 **16.** 24 **17.** 1 **18.** 39 **19.** -12 **20.** 21

Page 30 Addition of Integers

1. 18 **2.** 10 **3.** 28 **4.** -87 **5.** 0 **6.** -7 **7.** 13 **8.** -4
9. -67 **10.** -70 **11.** 42 **12.** -73 **13.** 4 **14.** -83
15. -93 **16.** 40 **17.** -103 **18.** -105 **19.** -90 **20.** 69

Page 31 Addition of Integers

1. -17 **2.** 80 **3.** -56 **4.** -43 **5.** -50 **6.** -26 **7.** -74
8. -69 **9.** -54 **10.** -97 **11.** 9 **12.** 20 **13.** -69
14. -52 **15.** -70 **16.** -108 **17.** -100 **18.** -125
19. -49 **20.** -66

Page 32 Addition of Integers

1. 9 **2.** -30 **3.** 0 **4.** -77 **5.** -16 **6.** -76 **7.** -14
8. 57 **9.** -158 **10.** 120 **11.** -120 **12.** -122 **13.** -34
14. -88 **15.** -117 **16.** -92 **17.** -122 **18.** 45 **19.** -34
20. 4

Page 33 Addition of Integers

1. -4 **2.** 8 **3.** 2 **4.** -5 **5.** 12 **6.** 1 **7.** 12 **8.** -22
9. 2 **10.** 10 **11.** 2 **12.** 12 **13.** -4 **14.** -19 **15.** 2
16. -5 **17.** -28 **18.** -33 **19.** 22 **20.** 16 **21.** -6
22. -2 **23.** -8 **24.** -14 **25.** 11 **26.** -18 **27.** -15
28. 13 **29.** -2 **30.** -8 **31.** 37 **32.** 61

Page 34 Addition of Integers

1. -10 **2.** -7 **3.** 17 **4.** 3 **5.** -22 **6.** 3 **7.** -15
8. -21 **9.** 23 **10.** -34 **11.** -21 **12.** 27 **13.** 32
14. -5 **15.** -8 **16.** -1 **17.** 3 **18.** -28 **19.** -37 **20.** 42
21. 17 **22.** 51 **23.** 52 **24.** -51 **25.** 39 **26.** 14 **27.** -38
28. -53 **29.** 13 **30.** -18 **31.** 77 **32.** 36

Page 35 Subtraction of Integers

1. 5 **2.** -13 **3.** -34 **4.** 44 **5.** 52 **6.** -81 **7.** -5
8. -11 **9.** -2 **10.** -13 **11.** 45 **12.** 61 **13.** 6 **14.** 12
15. 113 **16.** 95 **17.** 1 **18.** 3 **19.** -113 **20.** -150
21. 129 **22.** 114 **23.** 84 **24.** 56 **25.** -33 **26.** -34
27. -47 **28.** -28 **29.** -98 **30.** -137 **31.** -82
32. -21

Page 36 Subtraction of Integers

1. 9 **2.** -17 **3.** 7 **4.** 21 **5.** -45 **6.** 93 **7.** -20 **8.** -20
9. -4 **10.** 64 **11.** 58 **12.** 57 **13.** -50 **14.** 17 **15.** 29
16. 71 **17.** 31 **18.** 28 **19.** 95 **20.** -70 **21.** 56
22. -9 **23.** 346 **24.** 27 **25.** -11 **26.** -34 **27.** -105
28. 44 **29.** -95 **30.** -69 **31.** -8 **32.** 85

Page 37 Addition and Subtraction of Integers

1. 23 **2.** -10 **3.** 38 **4.** -50 **5.** -33 **6.** 85 **7.** 40
8. -91 **9.** 66 **10.** 25 **11.** -25 **12.** 43 **13.** -25
14. -39 **15.** -13 **16.** 32 **17.** 80 **18.** 137 **19.** -34
20. 95 **21.** 135 **22.** 106 **23.** -82 **24.** -121 **25.** -92
26. -100 **27.** 15 **28.** -39 **29.** -149 **30.** -177
31. 18 **32.** -9

Page 38 Addition and Subtraction of Integers

1. 56 **2.** -2 **3.** 51 **4.** -69 **5.** 9 **6.** 93 **7.** 32 **8.** -94
9. 106 **10.** -38 **11.** -50 **12.** 38 **13.** -35 **14.** -47
15. -47 **16.** -13 **17.** 86 **18.** 115 **19.** -23 **20.** 133
21. 81 **22.** 90 **23.** -70 **24.** -92 **25.** -125 **26.** -61
27. 28 **28.** 13 **29.** -120 **30.** -111 **31.** 46 **32.** -47

Page 39 Addition and Subtraction of Integers

1. 40 **2.** 15 **3.** -85 **4.** 53 **5.** 1 **6.** -19 **7.** 120
8. -147 **9.** -130 **10.** 105 **11.** -45 **12.** -33 **13.** 9
14. 20 **15.** -25 **16.** -11 **17.** -92 **18.** -104 **19.** 125
20. 129 **21.** -118 **22.** -95 **23.** 130 **24.** 105 **25.** -61
26. -80 **27.** 23 **28.** -170 **29.** -142 **30.** -173
31. -11 **32.** 24 **33.** 5 **34.** -8 **35.** 23 **36.** 11 **37.** -83
38. -32 **39.** -9 **40.** 133 **41.** 10 **42.** 6 **43.** 31
44. -73 **45.** 65 **46.** 60

Page 40 Addition and Subtraction of Integers

1. 48 **2.** 42 **3.** 57 **4.** 77 **5.** 18 **6.** 53 **7.** 141 **8.** -158
9. -153 **10.** -129 **11.** 18 **12.** -53 **13.** 16 **14.** 23
15. -35 **16.** -33 **17.** -123 **18.** -94 **19.** 152
20. 113 **21.** -90 **22.** -120 **23.** 140 **24.** 140 **25.** -37
26. -75 **27.** -57 **28.** -160 **29.** -139 **30.** -125 **31.** -6
32. 119 **33.** -9 **34.** -52 **35.** 50 **36.** 63 **37.** -72
38. 40 **39.** -31 **40.** 27 **41.** 23 **42.** 32 **43.** -134
44. -65 **45.** 73 **46.** 27

Page 41 Addition and Subtraction of Integers

1. –3 2. –16 3. –17 4. –7 5. 29 6. –29 7. 15
8. 14 9. –16 10. –9 11. 8 12. 0 13. –31 14. –46
15. 34 16. –54 17. –45 18. –63 19. 48 20. 1
21. 27 22. –32 23. 6 24. –78 25. 19 26. 89 27. –71
28. –14 29. 45 30. 46 31. –22 32. –34 33. –39
34. –35 35. 16 36. –53 37. –87 38. –80 39. –108
40. –203 41. –128 42. –132 43. 12 44. –17 45. –191
46. 35 47. 108 48. –121

Page 42 Addition and Subtraction of Integers

1. 1 2. –6 3. –4 4. 4 5. 16 6. –42 7. 12 8. 32
9. –4 10. –6 11. 24 12. 2 13. –12 14. –50 15. 15
16. –89 17. –27 18. –67 19. 71 20. –9 21. 58 22.
10 23. –21 24. –74 25. 57 26. 153 27. –14 28. 12
29. 5 30. 96 31. –12 32. –28 33. –65 34. 45 35. –9
36. 69 37. –76 38. –178 39. –86 40. –186 41. –114
42. –79 43. –110 44. –20 45. –51 46. –38 47. 175
48. –28

Page 43 Multiplication of Integers

1. –21 2. 12 3. 156 4. –385 5. –66 6. –161 7. 378
8. 456 9. –352 10. –375 11. 240 12. 1092 13. –1260
14. –3080 15. 2618 16. 11136 17. –50 18. –62 19.
675 20. 919 21. –850 22. –612 23. 360 24. 277
25. –465 26. 228 27. –139 28. –96 29. –221 30.
–181 31. –180 32. –360

Page 44 Multiplication of Integers

1. –45 2. –120 3. 272 4. 91 5. 60 6. –152 7. –252
8. 308 9. –429 10. –495 11. –105 12. 1408 13.
13440 14. 29106 15. –59211 16. –34112 17. 5 18.
27 19. 72 20. 663 21. –577 22. –477 23. 525
24. 696 25. –838 26. –41 27. 420 28. 417 29.
1067 30. 679 31. –88 32. –378

Page 45 Evaluating Variable Expressions

1. –42 2. 0 3. –13 4. 14 5. 21 6. –28 7. 35
8. –27 9. 8 10. –1 11. 43 12. –48 13. –47 14. –56
15. –20 16. 14 17. 45 18. 111 19. 12 20. 8 21. –6
22. 6 23. 32 24. 31 25. 124 26. 118 27. –366 28.
–939 29. 378 30. –915 31. 5 32. 57 33. –36 34.
–83

Page 46 Evaluating Variable Expressions

1. 24 2. –40 3. 16 4. –12 5. 37 6. –19 7. –21 8. 6
9. –15 10. 40 11. 137 12. 99 13. –240 14. 0
15. 26 16. –5 17. 16 18. 9 19. 39 20. –115 21. 0
22. 106 23. 55 24. –96 25. 218 26. –272 27. 415
28. –569 29. 3876 30. –760 31. 84 32. 22 33. –79
34. –69

Page 47 Reciprocals

1. –(1/5) 2. 1/6 3. –(1/12) 4. 1/15 5. 3 6. –7 7. –4
8. –5 9. –6 10. 13 11. 25 12. –17 13. 26 14.
–47 15. –36 16. –53 17. –16 18. 45 19. 5/4 20.
–(3/2) 21. –(7/8) 22. 10/9 23. 120 24. –72 25. –55
26. –225

Page 48 Reciprocals

1. 1/25 2. –(1/37) 3. 1/105 4. none 5. 27 6. –22
7. –17 8. 7 9. –23 10. 15 11. –25 12. –16 13.
29 14. –24 15. –17 16. –22 17. –17 18. 29 19. 3/7
20. –(9/2) 21. –(18/17) 22. 29/21 23. 60 24. –104
25. –65 26. –275

Page 49 Operations with Numbers

1. 3 2. 28 3. 21 4. –(1/32) 5. –(5/96) 6. –18
7. –(1/105) 8. –(1/84) 9. –70 10. 13/23 11. –(36/5)
12. –5 13. 1 14. –(5/3) 15. –8 16. 10 17. 0 18. –12
19. 3/25 20. 25/16 21. –(1/240) 22. –(1/15)
23. –(22/45) 24. –(1/20) 25. 1/4 26. –(25/12)

Page 50 Operations with Numbers

1. 5 2. 45 3. 18 4. –(1/64) 5. –(1/20) 6. –14
7. –(1/48) 8. –(1/56) 9. –20 10. 58/63 11. 18
12. –(9/2) 13. 16/3 14. 16/3 15. –(43/2) 16. 22
17. –(1/2) 18. 28 19. –4 20. 5/8 21. 1/200 22. 5/8
23. 13/2 24. 21/20 25. 6 26. 11/16

Page 51 Number Properties

1. C 2. B 3. G 4. D 5. I 6. G 7. C 8. I 9. A
10. B 11. E 12. F 13. G 14. B 15. K 16. G 17. D
18. K 19. G 20. D 21. B 22. J

Page 52 Number Properties

1. I 2. G 3. C 4. K 5. B 6. K 7. G 8. E
9. D 10. A 11. J 12. I 13. B 14. C 15. B
16. G 17. F 18. D 19. K 20. I 21. G 22. E

Page 53 Using Number Properties

1. $4x + 4y$ 2. $24m + 32n$ 3. $14x + 21y$ 4. $3r + 5s$
5. $9x + 12y$ 6. $270 + 50a$ 7. $160 + 130x$ 8. $2 + a$
9. $3ab + 7a$ 10. $2mn + 15m$ 11. $7(a + b)$ 12. $8(x + y)$
13. $5(2c + d)$ 14. $5(4m + 3n)$ 15. $x(20 + 1) = 21x$
16. $x(25 + 9) = 34x$ 17. $a(12 + 16) = 28a$ 18. $2m(13 + 9)$
$= 44m$ 19. $4(1 + t)$ 20. $9(1 + x)$ 21. $14ab$ 22. $-15bcm$
23. $30x^2y^2$ 24. $-56a^3b$ 25. $-286a^2b^2$ 26. $35c^3d^2$
27. $-120ab^2c$ 28. $504x^2y^2$

Page 54 Using Number Properties

1. $5a + 5b$ 2. $18r + 63s$ 3. $-20c - 8d$ 4. $6x + 9y$
5. $10x + 14y$ 6. $-51 - 39m$ 7. $143 - 117z$ 8. $3 - c$
9. $5xy + 2xz$ 10. $2mn + 15m$ 11. $9(x + y)$ 12. $5(a + b)$
13. $4(3c - 2d)$ 14. $15(2m - n)$ 15. $x(15 + 7) = 22x$
16. $r(17 + 12) = 29r$ 17. $6a(3 + 4) = 42a$
18. $3c(5 + 4) = 27c$ 19. $9(1 - z)$ 20. $13(1 - x)$ 21. $-70abc$
22. $30abd$ 23. $-64m^2n^2$ 24. $-105x^2y^2$ 25. $-64a^2b^2c^2$
26. $120cd^3$ 27. $-48x^3y^2$ 28. $-576m^3n^2$

Page 55 Combining Like Terms

1. $20a$ 2. $39x$ 3. $2y$ 4. $-4c$ 5. $90x + 4$ 6. $52y + 10$
7. $40ab$ 8. $37mn$ 9. $-19abc$ 10. $-18rst$
11. $16a - 9c$ 12. $-5x + 22y$ 13. $7c + 5$ 14. $-2r + 8$
15. $6x + 36$ 16. $16n + 76$ 17. $-2xy + 7x$ 18. $22bc - 11c$
19. x^2y 20. $17x^3$ 21. $8x^2y + 3$ 22. $11a^2b - 7$
23. $x^2 + 6x$ 24. $-2m^3 + 2m^2 - 8m$ 25. $7xy - 6yz$
26. $23rs - 14st$ 27. $7x^2 - 5xy + 4y^2$ 28. $a^2 - 3ab + b^2$
29. $6a^2b + 7$ 30. $33c^3d - 9$ 31. $18x^2 - 14x$
32. $9y^3 - 2y^2$

Page 56 Combining Like Terms

1. $26x$ 2. $38c$ 3. $2y$ 4. $11z$ 5. $75a + 25$ 6. $45r + 12$
7. $13xy$ 8. $-15cd$ 9. $-12xyz$ 10. $11cde$ 11. $13x - 26y$
12. $-4c + 5d$ 13. $-26a + 7$ 14. $-36m + 3$ 15. $18c - 54$
16. $30x - 9$ 17. $17ab - 4b$ 18. $-8rs - 36s$ 19. $-4x^2y$
20. $22a^3$ 21. $25m^2n - 15$ 22. $-52c^2d + 9$ 23. $66a^2 - b$
24. $3x^3 - 11y^2$ 25. $3r^2s$ 26. $3ab^3$ 27. $-9xy^2 + 10x^2y$
28. $19a^2b - 7ab^2$ 29. $56x^2 - 22y$ 30. $7a^2 + 16b^2$
31. $19abc^2$ 32. $-145x^2y^2z$

110

Page 57 Checking for Solutions

1. 2 **2.** 3 **3.** 1, 2, 3, 4 **4.** 2, 4, 6, 8 **5.** 1 **6.** 4 **7.** 0
8. 5 **9.** –2, –1, 0, 1, 2 **10.** ∅ **11.** ∅ **12.** ∅
13. 3 **14.** 3 **15.** –3 **16.** –2 **17.** ∅ **18.** 4 **19.** 3
20. 4 **21.** 1 **22.** 3 **23.** ∅ **24.** ∅ **25.** –1, 1 **26.** – 4, 4
27. 3 **28.** ∅ **29.** 9 **30.** 7

Page 58 Checking for Solutions

1. 1 **2.** 2 **3.** ∅ **4.** 2, 4, 6, 8 **5.** 2 **6.** 1 **7.** –2, –1, 0, 1, 2 **8.** ∅ **9.** –2 **10.** –1 **11.** –1 **12.** 0 **13.** 4 **14.** 4
15. –2 **16.** –3 **17.** –1 **18.** ∅ **19.** 4 **20.** 2 **21.** 0
22. ∅ **23.** 4 **24.** 1 **25.** 8 **26.** 9 **27.** 1 **28.** ∅ **29.** 6
30. 3

Page 59 Solutions of Equations

1. $x = 4$ **2.** $x = 23$ **3.** $x = 25$ **4.** $x = 57$ **5.** $x = -37$
6. $x = -29$ **7.** $x = -29$ **8.** $x = -19$ **9.** $x = 90$ **10.** $x = 107$
11. $x = 55$ **12.** $x = 80$ **13.** $x = -39$ **14.** $x = -39$
15. $x = 8$ **16.** $x = 16$ **17.** $x = 23$ **18.** $x = 39$ **19.** $x = -19$
20. $x = -34$ **21.** $x = 5$ **22.** $x = 16$ **23.** $x = -30$
24. $x = -18$ **25.** $x = -36$ **26.** $x = -50$ **27.** $x = -11$
28. $x = -11$ **29.** $x = -23$ **30.** $x = -25$ **31.** $x = -7$
32. $x = -14$

Page 60 Solutions of Equations

1. $x = 69$ **2.** $x = 19$ **3.** $x = 35$ **4.** $x = 42$ **5.** $x = -60$
6. $x = -38$ **7.** $x = -20$ **8.** $x = -1$ **9.** $x = 70$
10. $x = 84$ **11.** $x = 159$ **12.** $x = 153$ **13.** $x = -17$
14. $x = -69$ **15.** $x = 30$ **16.** $x = 27$ **17.** $x = 35$ **18.** $x = 58$
19. $x = -29$ **20.** $x = -54$ **21.** $x = -2$ **22.** $x = 16$
23. $x = -38$ **24.** $x = -19$ **25.** $x = -37$ **26.** $x = -42$
27. $x = -14$ **28.** $x = -9$ **29.** $x = -29$ **30.** $x = -12$
31. $x = -24$ **32.** $x = -27$

Page 61 Solutions of Equations

1. $x = 3/4$ **2.** $x = 7/3$ or 2-1/3 **3.** $x = 2$ **4.** $x = 6/5$ or 1-1/5
5. $x = 9/8$ or 1-1/8 **6.** $x = 4/3$ or 1-1/3 **7.** $x = 38/7$ or 5-3/7
8. $x = 71/6$ or 11-5/6 **9.** $x = 47/8$ or 5-7/8
10. $x = 82/11$ or 7-5/11 **11.** $x = 11/8$ or 1-3/8
12. $x = 3/2$ or 1-1/2 **13.** $x = 1/9$ **14.** $x = -(1/8)$
15. $x = 6/5$ or 1-1/5 **16.** $x = 7/3$ or 2-1/3 **17.** $x = 0.75$
18. $x = 3.18$ **19.** $x = 9.75$ **20.** $x = 14. 19$ **21.** $x = -6.71$
22. $x = -8.62$ **23.** $x = -2.46$ **24.** $x = -2.12$ **25.** $x = -5.9$
26. $x = -12.4$ **27.** $x = 1.22$ **28.** $x = 7.94$ **29.** $x = 1.3$
30. $x = 3.5$ **31.** $x = 11.51$ **32.** $x = 17.65$

Page 62 Solutions of Equations

1. $x = 2/3$ **2.** $x = 5/4$ or 1-1/4 **3.** $x = 2$ **4.** $x = 1$
5. $x = 12/5$ or 2-2/5 **6.** $x = 2/3$ **7.** $x = -(21/5)$ or-(4-1/5)
8. $x = -(27/4)$ or –(6-3/4) **9.** $x = 23/7$ or 3-2/7
10. $x = 19/9$ or 2-1/9 **11.** $x = 5/6$ **12.** $x = 11/8$ or 1-3/8
13. $x = -(13/8)$ or –(1-5/8) **14.** $x = -(3/2)$ or –(1-1/2)
15. $x = 8/7$ or 1-1/7 **16.** $x = 6/5$ or 1-1/5 **17.** $x = 0.65$
18. $x = 0.69$ **19.** $x = 1.75$ **20.** $x = -9.34$ **21.** $x = -3.65$
22. $x = -6.32$ **23.** $x = -3.18$ **24.** $x = -1.56$ **25.** $x = -11.4$
26. $x = -9.5$ **27.** $x = -3.69$ **28.** $x = -5.49$ **29.** $x = -3.3$
30. $x = -0.6$ **31.** $x = 9.52$ **32.** $x = 7.92$

Page 63 Solutions of Equations

1. $x = 2$ **2.** $x = 2$ **3.** $x = -2$ **4.** $x = -3$ **5.** $x = 7$ **6.** $x = 7$
7. $y = -14$ **8.** $y = -12$ **9.** $z = -1$ **10.** $z = -3$ **11.** $u = 0$
12. $u = 0$ **13.** $p = 8$ **14.** $p = 7$ **15.** $x = -115$
16. $x = -108$ **17.** $x = 1/2$ **18.** $x = 3$ **19.** $x = -(1/5)$

20. $x = -(1/4)$ **21.** $x = 1/7$ **22.** $x = 1/6$ **23.** $x = -4$
24. $x = -20$ **25.** $x = 3/4$ **26.** $x = 4/3$ **27.** $x = -(2/5)$
28. $x = -(3/4)$ **29.** $x = -(5/2)$ or –(2-1/2)
30. $x = -(3/2)$ or –(1-1/2) **31.** $x = 8/3$ or 2-2/3
32. $x = 5/4$ or 1-1/4

Page 64 Solutions of Equations

1. $x = 3$ **2.** $x = 4$ **3.** $x = -4$ **4.** $x = -7$ **5.** $x = 6$ **6.** $x = 6$
7. $x = -12$ **8.** $x = -12$ **9.** $z = 7$ **10.** $z = -9$ **11.** $u = 2$
12. $u = 3$ **13.** $p = 0$ **14.** $p = 0$ **15.** $x = 14$ **16.** $x = 99$
17. $x = 1/6$ **18.** $x = 1/3$ **19.** $x = -(1/6)$ **20.** $x = -(1/4)$
21. $x = 1/2$ **22.** $x = 1/7$ **23.** $x = -7$ **24.** $x = -14$
25. $x = 8/15$ **26.** $x = 5/8$ **27.** $x = -(2/5)$ **28.** $x = -(1/2)$
29. $x = -(3/2)$ or –(1-1/2) **30.** $x = -(14/5)$ or –(2-4/5)
31. $x = 4/3$ or 1-1/3 **32.** $x = 3/4$

Page 65 Solutions of Equations

1. $x = 10$ **2.** $x = 6$ **3.** $x = 12$ **4.** $x = 5$ **5.** $x = -21$
6. $x = -12$ **7.** $x = -8$ **8.** $x = -27$ **9.** $x = -8$ **10.** $x = -10$
11. $x = -28$ **12.** $x = -27$ **13.** $x = 14$ **14.** $x = 63$
15. $x = 30$ **16.** $x = 12$ **17.** $z = 32$ **18.** $z = 20$ **19.** $k = 36$
20. $k = 24$ **21.** $a = -54$ **22.** $b = -70$ **23.** $c = 45$
24. $d = -42$ **25.** $e = -40$ **26.** $f = -56$ **27.** $x = 160$
28. $y = 105$ **29.** $x = 99$ **30.** $y = 56$ **31.** $a = -143$
32. $x = -77$

Page 66 Solutions of Equations

1. $x = 8$ **2.** $x = 15$ **3.** $x = 18$ **4.** $x = 10$ **5.** $x = -7$
6. $x = -24$ **7.** $x = -18$ **8.** $x = -35$ **9.** $x = -6$ **10.** $x = -56$
11. $x = -30$ **12.** $x = 0$ **13.** $x = 28$ **14.** $x = 14$ **15.** $x = 0$
16. $x = 16$ **17.** $z = 30$ **18.** $z = 90$ **19.** $k = 35$
20. $k = 49$ **21.** $a = -48$ **22.** $b = -75$ **23.** $c = 21$
24. $d = -25$ **25.** $e = -30$ **26.** $f = -77$ **27.** $x = 30$ **28.** $y = 36$
29. $x = 49$ **30.** $y = 72$ **31.** $a = -165$ **32.** $x = -143$

Page 67 Solutions of Equations

1. $x = 8$ **2.** $x = 6$ **3.** $x = 4$ **4.** $x = 9$ **5.** $x = 2$
6. $x = 2$ **7.** $x = 2$ **8.** $x = 2$ **9.** $x = -4$ **10.** $x = -4$
11. $x = 2$ **12.** $x = 5$ **13.** $x = -6$ **14.** $x = -4$ **15.** $x = -8$
16. $x = 55$ **17.** $x = 3$ **18.** $x = 3$ **19.** $x = -7$ **20.** $x = -8$
21. $x = 6$ **22.** $x = 3$ **23.** $x = -13$ **24.** $x = -9$ **25.** $x = 14$
26. $x = 18$ **27.** $x = -5$ **28.** $x = -6$ **29.** $x = 6$ **30.** $x = 5$
31. $x = -1$ **32.** $x = -2$

Page 68 Solutions of Equations

1. $x = 5$ **2.** $x = 3$ **3.** $x = 6$ **4.** $x = 11$ **5.** $x = 5$ **6.** $x = 5$
7. $x = 11$ **8.** $x = 3$ **9.** $x = -6$ **10.** $x = -8$ **11.** $x = 7$
12. $x = 9$ **13.** $x = -8$ **14.** $x = -4$ **15.** $x = 13$ **16.** $x = 21$
17. $x = 7$ **18.** $x = 10$ **19.** $x = -6$ **20.** $x = -6$ **21.** $x = 7$
22. $x = 9$ **23.** $x = -6$ **24.** $x = -9$ **25.** $x = 12$ **26.** $x = 13$
27. $x = -11$ **28.** $x = -17$ **29.** $x = 19$ **30.** $x = 7$
31. $x = -15$ **32.** $x = -9$

Page 69 Solutions of Equations

1. $x = 15$ **2.** $x = 32$ **3.** $x = 42$ **4.** $x = 45$ **5.** $x = -16$
6. $x = -52$ **7.** $x = -154$ **8.** $x = -210$ **9.** $x = 65$
10. $x = 24$ **11.** $x = 40$ **12.** $x = 18$ **13.** $x = -63$
14. $x = 15$ **15.** $x = -8$ **16.** $x = -15$ **17.** $x = 32$
18. $x = 72$ **19.** $x = 3$ **20.** $x = 8$ **21.** $x = -10$
22. $x = -16$ **23.** $x = -20$ **24.** $x = -28$ **25.** $x = 28$ **26.** $x = 30$
27. $x = 48$ **28.** $x = 133$ **29.** $x = -27$ **30.** $x = -24$
31. $x = 248$ **32.** $x = 105$

Page 70 Solutions of Equations

1. $x = 8$ **2.** $x = 72$ **3.** $x = 80$ **4.** $x = 63$ **5.** $x = -70$
6. $x = -28$ **7.** $x = -26$ **8.** $x = 60$ **9.** $x = 35$ **10.** $x = 8$
11. $x = 16$ **12.** $x = 42$ **13.** $x = -24$ **14.** $x = -24$
15. $x = -25$ **16.** $x = 14$ **17.** $x = 14$ **18.** $x = 3$ **19.** $x = 10$
20. $x = 8$ **21.** $x = -6$ **22.** $x = -6$ **23.** $x = -10$ **24.** $x = 6$
25. $x = 21$ **26.** $x = 35$ **27.** $x = 54$ **28.** $x = 40$
29. $x = -18$ **30.** $x = -9$ **31.** $x = 168$ **32.** $x = -15$

Page 71 Solutions of Equations

1. $x = -6$ **2.** $x = 8$ **3.** $x = 6$ **4.** $x = 3$ **5.** $x = -16$
6. $x = -6$ **7.** $x = -6$ **8.** $x = -7$ **9.** $x = 8$ **10.** $x = 7$
11. $x = 6$ **12.** $x = 3$ **13.** $x = 2$ **14.** $x = -4$ **15.** $x = 4$
16. $x = 4$ **17.** $x = 3$ **18.** $x = 5$ **19.** $x = -7$ **20.** $x = -7$
21. $x = -6$ **22.** $x = -8$ **23.** $x = 6$ **24.** $x = 8$ **25.** $x = 2$
26. $x = 3$ **27.** $x = -8$ **28.** $x = -4$ **29.** $x = -7$ **30.** $x = -9$
31. $x = 2$ **32.** $x = 2$

Page 72 Solutions of Equations

1. $x = 9$ **2.** $x = -2$ **3.** $x = -2$ **4.** $x = 2$ **5.** $x = 7$ **6.** $x = 2$
7. $x = -4$ **8.** $x = -6$ **9.** $x = 10$ **10.** $x = -2$ **11.** $x = -3$
12. $x = 7$ **13.** $x = -2$ **14.** $x = 17$ **15.** $x = 9$ **16.** $x = 9$
17. $x = 4$ **18.** $x = 9$ **19.** $x = -3$ **20.** $x = -2$ **21.** $x = 8$
22. $x = 6$ **23.** $x = 4$ **24.** $x = 9$ **25.** $x = -2$ **26.** $x = -7$
27. $x = -3$ **28.** $x = -7$ **29.** $x = -4$ **30.** $x = -6$ **31.** $x = -8$
32. $x = -7$

Page 73 Solutions of Equations

1. $x = 10$ **2.** $x = 9$ **3.** $x = 5$ **4.** $x = -17$ **5.** $x = -7$
6. $x = -4$ **7.** $x = -3$ **8.** $x = 1$ **9.** $x = -2$ **10.** $x = 11$
11. $x = 13$ **12.** $x = 8$ **13.** $x = 1$ **14.** $x = 1$ **15.** $x = 4$
16. $x = 3$ **17.** $x = 2$ **18.** $x = -2$ **19.** $x = -16$ **20.** $x = -19$
21. $x = -25$ **22.** $x = 28$ **23.** $x = 12$ **24.** $x = -2$
25. $x = -10$ **26.** $x = 0$ **27.** $x = 2$ **28.** $x = -2$ **29.** $x = -2$
30. $x = 2$ **31.** $x = -3$ **32.** $x = 5$

Page 74 Solutions of Equations

1. $x = 9$ **2.** $x = 2$ **3.** $x = 3$ **4.** $x = 3$ **5.** $x = 5$
6. $x = -7$ **7.** $x = -9$ **8.** $x = 4$ **9.** $x = 3$ **10.** $x = 7$
11. $x = 1$ **12.** $x = 2$ **13.** $x = 3$ **14.** $x = -5$ **15.** $x = -8$
16. $x = 3$ **17.** $x = -1$ **18.** $x = -3$ **19.** $x = 1$ **20.** $x = -4$
21. $x = 3$ **22.** $x = 2$ **23.** $x = -22$ **24.** $x = 0$ **25.** $x = -5$
26. $x = 2$ **27.** $x = 0$ **28.** $x = 3$ **29.** $x = 1$ **30.** $x = 2$
31. $x = -3$ **32.** $x = -6$

Page 75 Solutions of Equations

1. $x = 1$ **2.** $x = 4$ **3.** $y = -3$ **4.** $y = -2$ **5.** $x = 4$ **6.** $z = 4$
7. $u = -18$ **8.** $p = 1/4$ **9.** $d = -1$ **10.** $m = 5$ **11.** $u = 5$
12. $u = 4$ **13.** $p = 1/3$ **14.** $p = 1/2$ **15.** $m = -22$
16. $m = -28$ **17.** $n = 2$ **18.** $n = -6$ **19.** $b = -4$ **20.** $b = -7$
21. $z = 10$ **22.** $z = 6$ **23.** $u = 3$ **24.** $u = 2$ **25.** $u = 3$
26. $u = 1$ **27.** $x = -21$ **28.** $u = 17$ **29.** $x = -5$ **30.** $x = -2$
31. $x = 1/3$ **32.** $x = -(1/2)$

Page 76 Solutions of Equations

1. $x = 7$ **2.** $x = 4$ **3.** $x = -3$ **4.** $y = -7$ **5.** $x = 2$ **6.** $z = 6$
7. $u = -11$ **8.** $p = 1$ **9.** $d = -5$ **10.** $m = 5$ **11.** $u = 11$
12. $u = 6$ **13.** $p = 2$ **14.** $p = -4$ **15.** $m = -4$ **16.** $m = 7$
17. $n = 1$ **18.** $n = -3$ **19.** $b = -2$ **20.** $b = -2$ **21.** $z = 3$
22. $z = 2$ **23.** $u = 2$ **24.** $u = 3$ **25.** $u = 4$ **26.** $u = -2$
27. $c = -7$ **28.** $c = -3$ **29.** $x = 65$ **30.** $x = 12$ **31.** $x = 3$
32. $x = 2$

Page 77 Writing and Solving Equations

1. $4 + 6 + 2 + z = 17$, $z = $ **5**
2. $z + 6 + 6 = 15$, $z = 3$
3. $6 + z + 9 + z + 1 = 22$, $z = 3$
4. $5 + z + 7 + z = 20$, $z = 4$
5. $8 + 5 + 10 + 4 + z = 30$, $z = $ **3**
6. $4z = 64$, $z = 16$
7. $5z + 4 + 9 = 28$, $z = 3$
8. $12 + z + 5 + z + 12 + 5 + 7 = 45$, $z = 2$
9. $z + 3 + z + z + 3 + 4 + 2 + 3 = 30$, $z = 5$
10. $z + z + 5 + z + 5 + z = 26$, $z = 4$
11. $z + 3 + 2 + z - 1 = 14$, $z = 5$
12. $z + 2 + 2z + 5 + z + 6 = 29$, $z = 4$

Page 78 Writing and Solving Equations

1. $x + 2 = 5$, $x = 3$, $y + 2 = 4$, $y = 2$, $P = 18$
2. $x + 3 = 10$, $x = 7$, $y + 5 = 9$, $y = 4$, $P = 38$
3. $x + 3 = 4$, $x = 1$, $y + 4 = 8$, $y = 4$, $P = 24$
4. $x = 6 + 2$, $x = 8$, $y + 6 = 11$, $y = 5$, $P = 38$
5. $4x = 12$, $x = 3$, $3y + 1 = 10$, $y = 3$, $P = 44$
6. $x = 4 + 5$, $x = 9$, $y = 3 + 4 + 3$, $y = 10$, $P = 48$
7. $2x + 3 = 11$, $x = 4$, $2y = 12$, $y = 6$, $P = 58$
8. $x + 8 = 10$, $x = 2$, $y = 2 + 7 + 2$, $y = 11$, $P = 42$
9. $x + 5 + 3 + 1 = 12$, $x = 3$, $y + 3 + 3 + 3 = 11$, $y = 2$, $P = 46$
10. $2x + 5 = 11$, $x = 3$, $y + 4 = 10$, $y = 6$, $P = 42$

Page 79 Solving Equations Having More Than One Variable

1. $b = c - a$ **2.** $y = z - x$ **3.** $y = r - 2m$ **4.** $u = v - 3t$
5. $a = c + b$ **6.** $x = z + y$ **7.** $b = a - c$ **8.** $y = x - z$
9. $t = (v - u)/2$ **10.** $x = (z - y)/2$ **11.** $x = 20 - 2y$
12. $a = 3(7 - b)$ **13.** $a = c/b$ **14.** $x = z/y$
15. $a = (c - 3)/b$ **16.** $x = (z + 4)/y$ **17.** $y = (x - z)/2$
18. $b = (a - c)/2$ **19.** $a = (c - 2b)/3$ **20.** $m = (p - 3n)/4$
21. $b = (c - 3a)/2$ **22.** $n = (p - 4m)/3$ **23.** $a = (c + 3b)/5$
24. $m = (p + 4n)/6$ **25.** $a = (2 - c)/b$ **26.** $x = (4 - z)/y$
27. $n = q/mp$ **28.** $b = d/ac$ **29.** $x = y(z - 2)$
30. $a = b(c - 3)$ **31.** $x = y(m - 2 + z)$
32. $a = b(t + 3 - c)$

Page 80 Solving Equations Having More Than One Variable

1. $m = p - 2n$ **2.** $m = (p - n)/2$ **3.** $a = c + 2b$
4. $a = (c + b)/2$ **5.** $b = (c - a)/2$ **6.** $a = c - 2b$
7. $c = b + d$ **8.** $d = c - z$ **9.** $x = (z + y)/3$
10. $x = (3z + 2y)/5$ **11.** $x = 3(5 - 2y)$ **12.** $x = 4(4 - 3y)$
13. $m = r/n$ **14.** $n = r/m$ **15.** $x = (z - 5)/y$
16. $a = (c + 4)/b$ **17.** $b = (a - 2c)/3$ **18.** $s = (r - t)/5$
19. $x = (7 - 3y)/4$ **20.** $y = (7 - 4x)/3$ **21.** $t = (2s - 4)/3$
22. $s = (4 + 3t)/2$ **23.** $m = (p + 7n)/4$ **24.** $a = (c + 3b)/8$
25. $b = (5a - c)/3$ **26.** $n = (6m - p)/4$ **27.** $a = (c - 2)/b$
28. $x = (z - 4)/y$ **29.** $x = yz$ **30.** $a = bc$
31. $m = n(4 - p)$ **32.** $r = s(8 - t)$

Page 81 Solving Equations Having More Than One Variable

1. $y = 7 - 2x$ **2.** $y = 9 - 4x$ **3.** $y = (9 + x)/4$
4. $y = (5 - 7x)/2$ **5.** $y = 3x - 12$ **6.** $y = (12 - 6x)/5$
7. $y = (-2x - 10)/3$ **8.** $y = (x + 3)/6$ **9.** $y = 2(6 - x)$
10. $y = 4(10 - x)$ **11.** $y = (3/2)(15 - 3x)$ **12.** $y = 7x - 13$
13. $y = 5(10 - x)$ **14.** $y = (6/5)(6 - 7x)$ **15.** $y = (7/3)(9 - 2x)$
16. $y = (4/3)(11 - 4x)$ **17.** $t = d/r$ **18.** $r = d/t$

19. $h = A/b$ **20.** $b = A/h$ **21.** $L = (P - 2w)/2$
22. $h = 2A/b$ **23.** $r = C/2\pi$ **24.** $h = V/\pi r^2$
25. $a = (2A - bh)/h$ **26.** $b = (2A - ah)/h$ **27.** $r = i/pt$
28. $R = E/I$ **29.** $n = 2S/(a + 1)$ **30.** $a = L - d(n - 1)$

Page 82 Solving Equations Having More Than One Variable

1. $y = 5 - 3x$ **2.** $y = 7 - 2x$ **3.** $y = (12 - 8x)/4 = 3 - 2x$
4. $y = (8 - 4x)/2 = 4 - 2x$ **5.** $y = 5x - 13$
6. $y = 8x - 13$ **7.** $y = (-3x - 13)/4$ **8.** $y = (7 + 5x)/3$
9. $y = 3(7 - 2x)$ **10.** $y = 2(4 - 5x)$ **11.** $y = (4/3)(7x - 5)$
12. $y = (3/2)(6x - 9)$ **13.** $y = 3(12 - x)$ **14.** $y = 7(10 - x)$
15. $y = (3/2)(4 - 5x)$ **16.** $y = (2/5)(9 - 7x)$
17. $c = p - a - b$ **18.** $H = V/LW$ **19.** $h = A/(b_1 + b_2)$
20. $b = 2V/ah$ **21.** $B = 3V/h$ **22.** $\pi = 3V/4r^3$
23. $s = P/4$ **24.** $d_1 = 2A/d_2$ **25.** $n = (S + 360)/180$
26. $r = (A - p)/pt$ **27.** $d = (L - a)/(n - 1)$ **28.** $a = (2S - n)/n$
29. $H = FL/W$ **30.** $h = 1000k/IE$

Page 83 Translating Word Expressions

1. $x + 18$ **2.** $y - 5$ **3.** $7 + x$ **4.** $y - 10$ **5.** $7 - x$ **6.** $5x$
7. $7/y$ **8.** $h - 2$ **9.** $m + 7$ **10.** $15 + x$ **11.** $20 - y$
12. $12x$ **13.** $23/n$ **14.** $5x$ **15.** $m + n$ **16.** $r - s$

Page 84 Translating Word Expressions

1. $r + 25$ **2.** $z - 12$ **3.** $9 + m$ **4.** $y - 11$ **5.** $x - 2$ **6.** $4m$
7. $y/10$ **8.** $3 - x$ **9.** $9 + 8$ **10.** $x + 20$ **11.** $z + 12$
12. $15c$ **13.** $46/x$ **14.** $6x$ **15.** $r + s$ **16.** $p - q$

Page 85 Translating Word Expressions

1. $z(x + y)$ **2.** $(k + 7)/v$ **3.** $m/(z + u)$ **4.** $abc - d$
5. $10x - p$ **6.** $2(n - 4)$ **7.** $ac + r$ **8.** $5(b - k)$ **9.** $14c - d$
10. $(r + 9)/k$ **11.** $7(d - 11)$ **12.** $a(b + c)$ **13.** $rs - u$
14. $s/(t + u)$ **15.** $5(r + s)$ **16.** $t(r - s)$

Page 86 Translating Word Expressions

1. $9r - t$ **2.** $4(m + 10)$ **3.** $(a + b)/c$ **4.** $yz - x$
5. $4(a - b)$ **6.** $(5 + x)/y$ **7.** $rs - c$ **8.** $3(p - q)$
9. $a(b - c)$ **10.** $z(7 - a)$ **11.** $rt + 6$ **12.** $7/(p + q)$
13. $3(5x - y)$ **14.** $5/(c + d)$ **15.** $mn + 8$ **16.** $a(7 + x)$

Page 87 Translating Algebraic Expressions

Answers may vary.

1. a times the sum of b and c **2.** the product of r and s decreased by 8 **3.** x times the difference between y and z **4.** the sum of r time s and t times u **5.** four less than the product of m and n **6.** j times the sum of w and v **7.** six more than u divided by p **8.** eleven times the difference between t and 17 **9.** the product of x and y subtracted from d **10.** the product of r and u subtracted from the sum of a and b **11.** the product of a and b added to the product of x and y **12.** the sum of r and t divided by the difference in r and t **13.** three less than the product of a, b, and c **14.** twenty-five less than the quotient of m and n **15.** the difference of t and b subtracted from j **16.** u times the difference of k and 5

Page 88 Translating Algebraic Expressions

Answers may vary.

1. m diminished by the product of r and s **2.** a times the sum of b and c **3.** the product of x and y added to the product of v and w **4.** a times the sum of c and d **5.** r times the difference of s and t **6.** eleven times the difference of v and 5 **7.** the difference of y and z subtracted from x **8.** the product of p and q divided by the product of r and t **9.** the difference of a and b times the sum of a and b **10.** 27 less than the product of r, s, and t **11.** the sum of x and y divided by the difference of x and y **12.** the difference in r and s times the sum of r and s **13.** r less than the difference in p and q **14.** m times the difference in p and q **15.** the product of k and s less than the sum of x and y **16.** the product of p and q less than r

Page 89 Translating Sentences into Equations

1. $n + 7 = 35$ **2.** $n + 5 = 17$ **3.** $5 = 2n - 6$ **4.** $6n - 7 = 10$
5. $n + 10 = 62$ **6.** $3n(12) = 20$ **7.** $(1/2)n = 16$
8. $n + 13 = 22$ **9.** $4 + 2n = 52$ **10.** $10n = 420$
11. $5n = 120$ **12.** $5 + 2n = 17$ **13.** $3n - 12 = 5$ **14.** $n + 5 = 17$
15. $6n(15) = 42$ **16.** $5n - 12 = 9$

Page 90 Translating Sentences into Equations

1. $(1/3)n = n - 12$ **2.** $2n/6 = 42$ **3.** $6(n - 4) = 25$
4. $(1/2)n = n - 7$ **5.** $45/n = 5$ **6.** $(1/3)n + 7 = 15$
7. $(1/3)n + 5 = 18$ **8.** $(3n - 9)/4 = 21$ **9.** $2n/4 = 25$
10. $(n + 12)/3 = 9$ **11.** $(n + 3)/5 = n + 2$ **12.** $5n + 16 = 24$
13. $(1/4)n + 6 = 15$ **14.** $5(n - 2) = 17$ **15.** $(n + 7)/2 = 19$
16. $(n + 7)/4 = n + 19$

Page 91 Number Problems

1. $n - 4 = 172$, $n = 176$ **2.** $n + 10 = -122$, $n = -132$
3. $n + 22 = -105$, $n = -127$ **4.** $n - 12 = 114$, $n = 126$
5. $n - 17 = 35$, $n = 52$ **6.** $n - 46 = 78$, $n = 124$
7. $n + 22 = 47$, $n = 25$ **8.** $n + 56 = 82$, $n = 26$
9. $n + 12 = 67$, $n = 55$ **10.** $n + 16 = 59$, $n = 43$
11. $n + 52 = -11$, $n = -63$ **12.** $n + 85 = -34$, $n = -119$
13. $n + 4 = 15$, $n = 11$ **14.** $n + 7 = 17$, $n = 10$
15. $n - 6 = 22$, $n = 28$ **16.** $n - 12 = -14$, $n = -2$

Page 92 Number Problems

1. $n - 7 = 114$, $n = 121$ **2.** $n + 4 = -95$, $n = -99$
3. $n + 35 = -116$, $n = -151$ **4.** $n - 18 = 76$, $n = 94$
5. $n - 11 = 28$, $n = 39$ **6.** $n - 55 = -16$, $n = 39$
7. $n + 47 = 51$, $n = 4$ **8.** $n + 19 = 51$, $n = 32$
9. $n + 20 = -12$, $n = -32$ **10.** $n + 32 = 75$, $n = 43$
11. $n + 75 = -106$, $n = -181$ **12.** $n + 23 = -45$, $n = -68$
13. $n + 50 = 13$, $n = -37$ **14.** $n + 29 = 15$, $n = -14$
15. $n - 9 = 53$, $n = 62$ **16.** $n - 16 = -27$, $n = -11$

Page 93 Problem Solving with Equations

1. 7 **2.** -6 **3.** 34 **4.** -18 **5.** -11 **6.** 5-1/2 **7.** 6 **8.** 11
9. 5 **10.** 3 **11.** 27 **12.** 1640 **13.** $6.00 **14.** $5.20

Page 94 Problem Solving with Equations

1. 9 **2.** 8 **3.** 30 **4.** -48 **5.** 20 **6.** -9 **7.** 9 **8.** 15 **9.** 4
10. 3 **11.** 35 **12.** 1473 **13.** $10.00 **14.** $7.26

Page 95 Motion Problems

1. 7 h **2.** 6 h **3.** 65 mi/h, 73 mi/h **4.** 58 mi/h, 69 mi/h **5.** 2 h **6.** 384 mi/h, 402 mi/h **7.** 7 h **8.** 3 h

Page 96   Motion Problems

1. 8 h   **2.** 5 h   **3.** 48 mi/h, 58 mi/h   **4.** 41 mi/h, 56 mi/h
5. 3 h   **6.** 350 mi/h, 382 mi/h   **7.** 6 h   **8.** 3 h

Page 97   Motion Problems

1. 6h, 5 h   **2.** 4-4/5 h, 8-4/5 h   **3.** 40 mi/h, 54 mi/h
4. 80 mi/h, 72 mi/h   **5.** 48 mi/h   **6.** 40 mi/h   **7.** 2 h
8. 1-1/3 h

Page 98   Motion Problems

1. 11-2/5 h, 10-2/5 h   **2.** 7 h, 12 h   **3.** 18-1/2 mi/h, 37-
1/2 mi/h   **4.** 45 mi/h, 51 mi/h   **5.** 70 mi/h   **6.** 56
mi/h   **7.** 3 h   **8.** 2 h

Page 99   Consecutive Integer Problems

1. 34, 35, 36   **2.** –42, –43, –44   **3.** –82, –83, –84, –85
4. 64, 65, 66, 67   **5.** 15, 16, 17   **6.** –25, –24, –23   **7.** 44,
46, 48   **8.** –102, – 104, –106   **9.** –71, –73, –75   **10.** 93, 95,
97   **11.** –4, –2, 0, 2   **12.** –3, –1, 1, 3

Page 100   Consecutive Integer Problems

1. 45, 46, 47   **2.** –37, –38, –39   **3.** –72, –73, –74, –75
4. 58, 59, 60, 61   **5.** 25, 26, 27   **6.** –37, –36, –35
7. 68, 70, 72   **8.** –122, –120, –118   **9.** 35, 37, 39
10. –23, –25, –27   **11.** –10, –8, –6, –4   **12.** 9, 11, 13, 15

Page 101   Problem Solving with Equations

1. 55, 71   **2.** 77, 108   **3.** 15, 31   **4.** 27, 50   **5.** 27 in., 49
in.   **6.** 33 cm, 76 cm   **7.** 18 h, 39 h   **8.** 34 h, 63 h   **9.** 16
years, 48 years   **10.** 25 years, 52 years   **11.** $43, $85,
$96   **12.** $27, $49, $51

Page 102   Problem Solving with Equations

1. 37, 53   **2.** 43, 61   **3.** 23, 49   **4.** 31, 53   **5.** 43 in., 82
in.   **6.** 27 cm, 64 cm   **7.** 15 h, 33 h   **8.** 21 h, 48 h
9. 13 years, 45 years   **10.** 23 years, 52 years
11. $37, $68, $75   **12.** $58, $112, $135

Page 103   Coin Problems

1. 19   **2.** 29   **3.** 4 dimes, 12 nickels   **4.** 12 dimes, 60
quarters   **5.** 15 nickels, 33 dimes, 42 quarters   **6.** 13
quarters, 22 dimes, 67 nickels   **7.** 18 quarters, 13 dimes,
6 nickels   **8.** 600 pennies, 175 nickels, 19 dimes, 95
quarters

Page 104   Coin Problems

1. 22   **2.** 37   **3.** 8 dimes, 13 nickels   **4.** 14 dimes, 35
quarters   **5.** 12 nickels, 29 dimes, 35 quarters   **6.** 21
quarters, 17 dimes, 48 nickels   **7.** 27 quarters, 17 dimes,
12 nickels   **8.** 800 pennies, 148 nickels, 25 dimes, 82
quarters

Page 105   Angle Problems

1. 34°, 56°   **2.** 17°, 73°   **3.** 37°, 143°   **4.** 47°, 133°
5. 35°, 67°, 78°   **6.** 55°, 55°, 70°   **7.** 58°, 122°
8. 49°, 131°

Page 106   Angle Problems

1. 29°, 61°   **2.** 37°, 53°   **3.** 48°, 132°   **4.** 31°, 149°
5. 28°, 63°, 89°   **6.** 45°, 45°, 90°   **7.** 47°, 133°
8. 63°, 117°